C000176849

A Life's

A Life's Tales

Joseph Hucknall

Paradise Press

First published in Great Britain in 2013 by
Paradise Press, BM Box 5700, London WC1N 3XX.
www.paradisepress.org.uk

Copyright © Joseph Hucknall 2013

The moral right of Joseph Hucknall to be identified as the author of this work has been asserted by him in accordance with the Copyright, Designs and Patents act 1988.

All rights reserved. No part of this publication may be reproduced, stored in a retrieval system, or be transmitted, in any form or by any means, electronic, mechanical, photocopying, recording or otherwise, without the prior permission of the copyright owner.

A CIP catalogue record for this book
is available from the British Library.

ISBN 978-1-904585-49-7

This book is also available to download as
an e-book from the Paradise Press website.

Printed and bound in Great Britain by Biddles, part of
the MPG Books Group, Bodmin and King's Lynn.

Cover artwork by Ramon Gonzalez.

ACKNOWLEDGEMENTS

With appreciation to the following for their advice and encouragement:

Sheena Joughin, Elisabeth Walford, Mo Endfield, Patricia Marmont, Margaret Crick, Ramon Gonzalez, John Dixon, Rod Shelton.

CONTENTS

‘There is nothing good or bad, but thinking makes it so.’

Hamlet: Act 2 Sc. 2 – Shakespeare

— One —

BORN INTO THE BUILDINGS

The extent of my world was the distance I could walk and, by the age of six in 1935, I had explored all the streets of the island. They were my playground and I tasted the tar from them before I tasted chewing gum. Their names reflected the town's shipbuilding origins: Schooner Street, Barque Street, Sloop Street, Ship Street, Steamer Street. Although identical in appearance, each street had its own character, which it owed to its inhabitants, past and present, dominated by tenement flats and collectively known as 'The Buildings'. Stark, brick-built, four-storied, gas-lit, heated by open fire ranges, with balconies-cum-washrooms, overlooking communal closes, eight flats to a close, built by workers for workers.

This was 'Old Barrow' Island, lying off the Furness peninsular in Cumberland, previously farmed by the Cistercian monks of Furness Abbey and later industrialised by Vickers Armstrong, shipbuilders, armament manufacturers and engineers. Brig Street was my street and 8c, the flat where I and my eight siblings were born, was third close along, second floor up. With seven brothers and sisters older than me and Reg, the baby, I knew of no families larger than mine. Fortunately, with only one bedroom, we were seldom all home at once.

As well as the bedroom, there was a living room, a small kitchen, a washroom and a toilet and, although we accepted our lot as ordained, we were not blind to the fact that some people were better off; they lived in flats with two bedrooms. Our parents had moved from Workington to Barrow for our father to find work and one bedroom answered to their needs and income. Unfortunately the size of the flat did not keep up with the size of the family.

Below us lived a wild Irish family, the Sidleys, not very clean, emitting a permanent smell of Irish stew and best avoided. Mam said they had cockroaches, so I never went in. Bed bugs and cockroaches were the most feared interlopers by Mam but, despite searching for them, I never found any. Mrs Sidley was obese and argumentative and lived most of her life sitting in a chair in the close, minding other people's business.

Next to them lived Mr & Mrs Holmes, who were old and had lived there forever. Mrs Holmes would give me a slice of bread and jam if I visited them, and Mr Holmes would light up his pipe and talk to me. Once he asked me to suck his pipe but it made me sick, and he said I would never want to smoke again.

'But my Dad smokes,' I retorted.

'Yes, Woodbines. Coffin nails,' he said derisively.

Across the landing from us, in a two bedroomed flat, lived the Kellet family, whom we all liked. Ma and Pa with a son and daughter. Pa Kellet drank tea from his saucer and slurped, but no one seemed to mind. When I did it, I was told off by Mam. Ma Kellet said she was my godmother but I never really understood what that was. How could I have two mothers? She told me she had helped to deliver me, which I never understood either, as I thought it was only the postman who delivered parcels, and Dad had said I came in a parcel. The Kellets were very friendly, and liked me to call on them, which I did very often.

Once, when I did, I got a big surprise.

'You will be having a baby brother or sister soon. Did you know?' said Ma Kellet.

No, I did not know. How could I, if no one had told me?

'Will it come in a parcel too?'

Both Ma and Pa laughed at each other. I was perplexed.

'Your mother's a good woman, but she's got her hands full, and you must help her all you can.'

'When is it going to be delivered?'

'Oh, it will not be before Christmas.'

Now why could it not be delivered at Christmas, along with the other presents, I wondered? But I refrained from asking. The news had left me speechless.

I crossed the landing and found Sarah, my sister, at home, attempting to knit.

'Am I having a baby brother?'

'You will be having a baby brother or a baby sister, or perhaps both.'

Ma Kellet had not mentioned that possibility. Could you have more than one baby?

'What can I do to help Mam?'

'Be invisible. Keep out of the way,' said Sarah, much to my surprise.

How could I become invisible?

It was January when I awoke one morning, and Mam, who unusually was still in bed, showed me two babies by her side.

'Hello Joe. You've got two little brothers now, Reginald and Ronald. Aren't they lovely?'

They did not look lovely to me, with their red screwed-up faces.

'Have they just come?' I asked, 'And where from?'

'No, they were delivered during the night.'

Another surprise. I did not know the postman delivered at night, but to have two brothers suddenly appearing was a much bigger surprise.

Mam stayed in bed for days afterwards and we had many visitors and neighbours calling to see the babies, and I did feel invisible as people did not seem to see me. Then one morning when I awoke, Sarah said that I would not see Ronald again.

'Why not?' I asked. I had already got to like the twins.

'He's gone back to where he came from,' said Sarah, between tears. 'He's died.'

I did not like to see Sarah crying, so I did not ask if he had gone back in a parcel.

Above us lived a lady on her own, Maud, who gave me a sweet whenever she passed me on the landing. I liked Maud, and I know she liked me. She was blond, wore red, and always smelled nice. Sometimes she went up to her flat with a man, and she never gave me a sweet then, but always a smile. Mam said that what she got up to wasn't right, and that I was never to go upstairs.

On the top floor lived two boys, William and his younger brother, David, but they were both older than me. Their mother was poorly and one day she died and their father had to bring them up. Mam used to ask them in sometimes to have a meal with us, or ask me to take them bread she had just baked. William and my sister Lena were the same age and very friendly. When he became sixteen and David was fourteen, a woman from Dr. Barnardo's arranged for them to go on a farm in Canada, and we were all very sad when they left, particularly Lena, who cried, but William promised to write to her as soon as he arrived.

I never got to know the other people above us as I only saw them when they passed me on the landing, and they were not very friendly. We played on the landing when it was raining and in winter nights with candles in lanterns, or in turnips hollowed out with slots cut to represent the eyes, mouth and nose. Sometimes, if it was wet, my older brother, George, would meet his friends there, and they would smoke cinnamon sticks and play the Jew's harp, pitch and toss, or just talk and laugh at each other's jokes. They laughed too, when Maud passed them on the stairs, and would call out after her, but never when there was a man with her.

The washroom too, was a good place to play when it

rained. A zinc bath tub hung on the wall, which we filled with hot water and bathed in once a week. The water was not changed but topped up with a kettle of hot water for the next one to bathe, but my older brothers and sisters who worked went to the baths. The zinc bath was good to play in, and with the wooden dolly legs inside it, I could stand on them and imagine that I was a captain of a ship. The washroom had an opening, with a handrail, through which I could look out onto the close and the street below, and see what was happening. On Mondays, when everyone did their washing, and it was dry, the close would be filled with washing hung on clothes lines operated on pulleys stretched across the close.

The cries of street vendors pushing handcarts could often be heard. Cries of 'Fish alive o', 'Live cockles and mussels' and 'Ice cream' would have women and children running out to buy. As winter approached the ice cream man turned to selling mushy peas and his cry gave way to 'Hot peas, hot peas, penny a pint'. A street singer, known as Danny Boy, because that was the song he always started with, would stand in the street, cap in hand, and some people would throw down pennies to him. A man with a flat wooden cart pulled by a thin grey horse, cried out 'Rag an' bones', and in exchange for a bundle of rags, he would give a goldfish or two in a jam jar. I got many goldfish but they never lived long.

Everything had its season. Children lived more in the streets than in their flats. Hopscotch and skipping was favoured by the girls. Marbles, football, tin can turkey, tag and conkers by the boys. Any attempt at cricket meant playing on a concrete or gravel surface. Between the backs of the tenements there were grassed spaces, which would have made ideal playgrounds, but they were railed off and inaccessible. I could never fathom out why there were no trees growing.

In hot weather, the boys made for the docks to swim in,

but the docks' policemen would chase them away. My older brother, Alfie, was terrified of policemen, and always crossed the road to avoid them. If he had been naughty he was told that a policeman would come for him. If I was naughty, I was told a black man would get me, but I never saw any, except at the pictures. We had a picture house on the island, where we would go on Saturdays for twopence. It was called the 'Bug Hut', because of the fleas that bit you.

On Sundays, Mam would send Alfie, Sarah, George and me to Sunday school at St John's, where we were all baptized, but we rarely arrived there. George never went, but played round the docks with his mates instead. Alfie, Sarah and I preferred the Mission Hall, run by Mr and Mrs Quiggin, who had a sweet stall in the market. The Mission Hall was a small angular building on a corner, with tiered seating around a small room, and the Quiggins told us biblical stories, and of missionary work in Africa. It was much more interesting than St John's. We were given little books on the scriptures and a bag of sweets, fruit drops, acid drops, and 'Mint Cake', which the Quiggins made.

We did venture to St John's, with feelings of guilt, when they gave a Christmas party for children, and in summer, when we had an outing by train to Greenodd on the coast. There we had egg and spoon races, and three leg races, when two children raced with a leg tied together. We were each given a bag of food and a bottle of pop, and the train journey made for a very exciting day.

There were train lines alongside the roads bordering the shipyards, with steam trains shunting to and fro, often with cargoes of iron ore, coal and steel. This industrial activity was fascinating to a six-year-old boy, and I remember venturing up the steps of a signal box and making friends with the signalman. He seemed to be master of all, with a bird's eye view of the area, and being able to direct engines with his numerous levers. He said when I was old enough I could be trained to be a signalman, and for many weeks I thought of little else.

In summer we made for the coast, and this meant crossing to Walney Island, a twelve mile long island lying off Barrow. It cost a penny to cross the bridge until 1935, the Silver Jubilee year of George V, when it was renamed the Jubilee Bridge and made free. Mam would make up the sandwiches, usually egg and cress, wrap the teapot in a tea cloth, put tea and sugar in twists of paper, and, pushing baby Reggie in the pram, we walked to the shore. Hot water to make the tea could be got for a penny a pot, or with a little patience, a fire could be made on the beach to boil a tin of water.

There was a choice of three beaches, but to call them beaches was a misnomer, as they consisted almost entirely of stones. By removing the larger stones and using these to build a wall, around knee height, allowed one to undress discreetly. They also served as a windbreaker from the prevailing winds from the Irish Sea, and it was usual to find a wall already made. So we settled into it, made it more habitable with towels, and proceeded to change into swimwear. Tiptoeing gingerly over stones, perhaps hand in hand with Sarah, feeling the cold water covering my feet, then experiencing a wave pounding against me, before the sea covered my head, did not make me want to learn to swim, and I never did, despite Sarah's attempts. I could not get back to the shelter of the windbreaker quickly enough.

Our favoured beach was on the north of the island where there was a shingle beach and sand dunes. A man had built a small wooden shack in the dunes to live in, and we knew him as the hermit. He was unkempt with long straggly black hair and beard, and sometimes we met him in the lanes, where he would stand and preach. There were winkles and cockles in abundance when the tide had just receded, if we could get them before the seagulls. Nearby was a hamlet of whitewashed stone houses, known as 'North Scale', so different to the brick buildings we lived in and with the remains of an old windmill and an iron horse trough still in use. There was also a wheelless charabanc which had been converted into a shop, where we spent our last remaining pennies on ice cream or sweets. This meant a long walk back home, tired and hungry, before we gathered round the kitchen table to feast on the boiled winkles and cockles, each with a pin in hand, to pick them out of the shells and sandwich them between slices of Mam's bread. A simple supper, but oh, the satisfaction of feasting on what we had gathered from the sea shore was the culmination of a day of riches.

— Two —

HARD TIMES

Names of streets associated with ships included the one and only shopping street on the Island named Anchor Road. As young as I was, I was beginning to be interested in shops and the business that went on inside. It was not always evident on the surface. My friend, Reginald Raybould and I, would often play in his father's fledgling wireless shop or in the stockroom behind, a mystery to a six-year-old, with its coils of wire, switches, wireless sets, batteries and gadgets. His uncle had a butcher's shop in the street and when it was closed he let us play in it after giving us sawdust to put on the floor to soak up the blood. Carcasses and bones made an interesting contrast to bells and batteries, but it was the draper's shop next door which held more of a fascination for me. It had an air of respectability at the front, so different from the business done at the back.

Above the front window was a varnished fascia board and the names 'Tooner & Dennison, Clothiers & Drapers', in elegant black script. It was the only clothing shop on the Island and unlike the butchers, bakers, grocery, sweet, fruit and vegetable shops in the street, customers seldom entered, giving it more of an air of mystery to me. I could never pass without looking into the window to see its odd display. There were always the same two disfigured models on view, a woman and a man, which were never moved. The mannequin leaned forward, appearing ready to fall over, which, much to my disappointment, it never did. It had one hand raised, as if in acknowledgement to a passer-by. Its nose was chipped and on the top of its head was a blond wig which was usually askew. In summer it would have on a floral dress, which failed to hide the cracks and chips on the arms and legs, which even to my young eye, detracted from its appeal. In winter it would be wrapped in a coat and sometimes with a fur muff on the hand, which previously raised, would be brought down to waist level. The other arm never moved from its rigidity alongside the body, evident to me that it was broken at the elbow. To the back of the window stood a man's model, without hair or shoes. Its nose was cracked, obviously having taken a knock, but as its head was turned towards the wall, it was only by stepping inside the entrance that the crack was revealed. In winter it was invariably dressed in a blue serge suit, sometimes with a white silk scarf hanging around the neck. As this was standard Sunday wear for the shipyard workers, it scarcely turned a head from any passer-by. In summer, jacket and trousers in beige and grey replaced the suit. Bright colours rarely made an appearance.

Other clothing was draped on hangers, strung from the ceiling or, like scarecrows, hung on T-shaped stands. One week when I passed, a clothes line had been put up across the window with garments hung from it like washing but it had gone the following week and I never saw it again. The side and front of the window were given to displaying stacks of towels and bedding which did not change with the seasons. A sign on the window stated 'Club Cheques Taken', which puzzled me until Mam said they were instead of money and she couldn't do without them. Other than this, the window display gave out no welcome or enticement to enter. Mr Dennison looked after the shop. He was a staid elderly man who, summer and winter, dressed in a black jacket and pinstripe trousers, which gave to the shop a respectability above itself, and not seen worn by anyone else in the town except by the undertakers.

However, whilst any business conducted at the front of the shop was done with the minimum of deference by Mr Dennison, it was the business done by Mr Tooner at the back which excited my curiosity. I first entered it with my mother who was carrying a bundle of clothing. In its dim light we were confronted by a high counter, above which I saw the head of a man with spectacles perched on the end of his nose.

'Can you tell me what you can give me on this, Mr Tooner?' asked my mother, handing over the bundle.

'Five shillings,' he said. He looked down at me with disdain. 'That's the best I can do.'

Mr Tooner took the bundle and turned his back on us. The counter was too high for me to see over.

'I'll take that,' said Mam without hesitation. 'Hopefully it will only be for a week.'

Outside the shop, I asked my mother what it was they sold.

'Nothing. They lend money in exchange for things.'

'Lend money?'

'Yes, pawnbrokers,' she said, and looking up at her, I could see her face flush with embarrassment as a passing neighbour smiled knowingly at her, so I kept silent.

It did not make sense until after several visits with my mother, usually with Dad's suit, to take it in or to collect it. Of far more interest to me were the visits on a Monday afternoon, when auctions were held in the back room. An air of excitement, mixed with the smells of mothballs and stale sweat, filled the room. It would be crowded with the locals hoping to pick up a bargain, or to retrieve an item on which a pledge had lapsed. Mr Tooner became much friendlier when he took the auction, making jokes as each item was held up.

'A bundle of bedding! Never seen a bug. Looking for a good home.'

'An almost new suit! Worn only once, for the wedding.'

'A nine carat gold wedding ring! Looking for its owner.'

There were titters but little laughter as we already knew his jokes. He obviously enjoyed auctioning the items off, more than he did taking them in. Then he was not open to offers. His first offer was his final one, and Mam said he knew the value of everything, but never offered more than half of it. Many times I accompanied my mother, either in apprehension to pawn something, or in excited anticipation of her bidding, but when venturing through that back door, I learnt too, that my mother's pride was always left behind.

Weddings took on a communal aspect when word went round that there was one on, perhaps in a nearby street. Women and children gathered eagerly to see the bride resplendent in white emerging from her home. Oo's and ah's rose approvingly from the women. Usually, coins were thrown to the onlookers. If none were forthcoming the cry of 'Shabby wedding, hard up, hard up. Shabby wedding, hard up, hard up', was repeatedly chanted by the children. Sometimes the pennies were heated on a shovel before being thrown, which caused an outcry but much laughter too when the foolhardy rushed forward and got their fingers burnt.

Weddings were not the only adult activities children involved themselves in. No excitement was missed. One flat in particular held a morbid fascination for me. In the dark of a winter's evening a rent collector had been murdered on the landing outside a flat and all the rent money stolen. My questioning of my siblings as to who had done it only met with silence, which only increased my curiosity, and I never did find out. Neighbours' quarrels, street fights, drunken behaviour, police visits, all brought inquisitive children running to the scene. Life in The Buildings became easier in the summer when families spilled out of the flats onto the streets. Chairs would be brought out and much gossiping went on amongst groups of neighbours. Mam said she had no time for gossiping but gave an ear to it nonetheless. Election time saw the participation of groups of children going round the streets shouting in support of a candidate, and not always a Labour one, but echoing their father's choice with the usual battle song, 'Vote, vote, vote for XXX. Put old XXX in the dock!'

— THREE —

BROTHERS AND SISTERS

The nine of us slept in the one bedroom at one time or another with our parents sleeping in the living room, but it was a room for more than just sleep. We were all born in the room, delivered either by a friendly neighbour acting as midwife, but capable from much experience, or, in one emergency, by our father.

It was a refuge where, in isolation, I could sob my heart out if I had committed a misdemeanor. It was a sickroom, where from being ill with pneumonia, chicken pox or measles, one could be nursed into the euphoria of convalescence. It had witnessed death too, of an infant brother, and of old Uncle Bill, who had fought in Russia in the White Army. He had lived alone, but in the last few weeks of his life he had prevailed upon my mother to 'take him in', and never stopped complaining until death silenced him.

Its occupancy was as fluid as the tide, receding when older siblings left home to work away, either eagerly or tearfully, and flowing back when they joyfully returned. Two double brass beds filled the room, one for the boys and one for the girls. There was little room for anything else, except a chair. Other furniture would have been superfluous, as little storage was needed for our clothes.

There were times of anguish, and of other emotions, some shared, some solitary. I remember at bedtime watching my mother shed a private tear as she sat in the chair looking out of the window, waiting to see my father coming home from the pub, anxious that he had not stayed there too long. More than once, she had seen him turn the corner talking to a woman of ill repute from the neighbourhood. In their pre-courting days my father had a following of admirers, being a 'bit of a lad', in the colloquial term, and this fed my mother's jealousy of other women. I was sure her jealousy was ill-founded, as Dad had fathered ten children by her and worked unceasingly to feed and clothe them, nevertheless her jealousy never left her. Her final pregnancy occurred unexpectedly when she was forty-five. My sister, Lena, who was then twenty-one, and still living at home, confronted our father in the bedroom.

'Are there not enough children? It's not fair on Mam to have any more!'

'Don't question me on how many children I have,' he said, turning on her.

It was never raised or questioned again. After all, which child would a parent choose to forgo? And there were twins on the way.

The firstborn of my brothers and sisters was Jack, in 1909, followed two years later by Beatrice, who forever after, was his most critical sibling. Her antipathy towards him was sealed when they were indentured together into farm service for a year, when she was aged fourteen. Dad took them to the nearby market town of Ulverston, where in the spring and autumn, a Hiring Fair was held. Men, women and children of working age congregated in the market square waiting and hoping, but in apprehension, for farmers to offer them employment. The men and boys would put a piece of straw in their mouths to indicate they were available for work.

'I cried my heart out,' Beatrice told me years later. 'I didn't want to go away from home, and certainly not with brother Jack.'

Domestic employment or 'in service' was often the only work available, other than work in the shipyard, and usually meant leaving home. The family benefited by having one less mouth to feed, one less child to accommodate, and a wage, however meagre, added to the family income.

It seemed a long way from home when Dad took them to the farm, although it was only thirty miles, and left them with the farmer and his wife, consoling them that they could return home after only six months if they did not like it.

Their time together did not endear her brother to Beatrice. She accused him of selfishness, lacking consideration, and of not looking after her as an older brother should. In return he found her sullen and resentful. They were both homesick most of the time, and hated the menial work they were given to do. Their one year indenture was cut to six months and although they were glad to be home they were barely speaking to one another. Later, Jack went into the shipyard to work, along with most of the population of the town. Beatrice went to Manchester to work as a maid to a family.

My next sister, Lena, was born at the outbreak of the First World War, in 1914, and was a happy contented child, until she too went away 'into service' at fourteen. This was to a doctor and his family in nearby Lancaster. She had only served a few weeks when she had an accident that severely bruised her upper thigh. Thinking that she would get well, she persevered at her job, without any attention or advice from the doctor. When the bruise failed to heal, the doctor paid her off and sent her home. Our distraught mother took her to the family doctor, a Dr Farmer, who in his customary brusque manner dismissed the seriousness of the injury. As the pain, swelling and colour of the leg continued to get worse, a further visit to the doctor resulted in the condition being diagnosed as serious and Lena was taken to hospital. Then it was found that gangrene had set in, and that to save her life, her leg had to be amputated above the knee. For many years throughout her adolescence Lena had to walk with a wooden crutch until enough money was saved to buy her an artificial leg.

My father's war service ensured that another child,

Minnie, was not born until 1919. It was the custom for children to be named after their parents or relatives, so the same names occurred in succeeding generations. My own name, Joseph, occurs in the family genealogy in every generation back to 1663. Minnie inherited an aunt's name, and despised it. Abbreviation to Min was occasionally made, but that was scarcely more acceptable. She was small anyway, and in addition, Minnie was a redhead, another attribute she objected to as a child, attracting disparaging shouts from other children. Cries of 'ginger', however, were preferred to shouts of 'baldy', when Minnie unfortunately caught head lice, and our father shaved her head to get rid of them. Going to school was a misery for many weeks before her hair grew again. It was little surprise that Minnie developed into a feisty character.

Dad gave us all a penny a week pocket money which went on buying sweets, but stealing food and fruit from outside shops was acceptable to appease our ever-hungry stomachs. My older brothers, George and Alf, knew how they could earn considerably more than the penny a week. The local industries generated a large amount of scrap metal and the smaller pieces, together with other industrial rubbish, was taken in trucks to a tip. At George's instigation, they collected scrap metal from the tip and sold it by the sackful to a local scrap metal dealer.

Age fourteen was for all of us the year of our emancipation, but none more so than for my brother George, who ran away from home at that age. His disappearance was reported to the police and he was eventually found fifty miles away, heading for Liverpool. After being brought back home by the police and severely dealt with by father by being strapped, it made him more determined and he made his second and, this time, successful attempt to get to Liverpool. There he signed on as a cabin boy on a merchant ship. Before sailing, however, he wrote a letter home, telling his parents what he had done and not to worry about him. He posted the letter the day the ship sailed for Accra, on the Gold Coast. He was beyond his parents reach, and, at fourteen, at the start of his naval career. Mother was reassured by her belief in folklore that he would never drown, because at birth his head had been covered by a caul. Fortunately he never did despite being at sea throughout the war.

Sarah, my fourth sister, was six years older than me and from my infancy became my nursemaid and escort, if at times a little careless with me. Once, when she took me out, she lost me in the town centre, and arrived home in tears without me. Fortunately for me, I was seen by a woman who knew me and took me home. Sarah too, left school at fourteen and went to Windermere to work in a hotel, as a maid. She experienced her initiation on her first night in her bedroom, which she shared with other women, when they stripped her naked, pinched her all over her body and laughed at her.

Alf, five years my senior, was the seventh child but demanded all of our mother's attention, crying when she was not around, and having to be dragged to school. He was left-handed, but found this no detriment as he developed a skill of woodworking and model making, which eventually led him to an apprenticeship as a patternmaker in the shipyard. During the war he transferred to aircraft and moved to Vickers-Armstrong Supermarine Works, the birthplace of the Spitfire fighter plane, in Hampshire, where he eventually became an aeronautical designer. He lived in digs, in Winchester, where he met and married his wife, Yvonne.

Before then, in 1936 at the age of twelve, he had confided in me that it was his dream to live in California. We had been to see 'Snow White' at the newly built Roxy cinema, which opened up to us a luxurious modern art deco world. We often went to the cinema together, and like millions more, Alf was captivated by the image of America portrayed on the screen. He realised his dream at the age of twenty-six, when he left for California, with his wife, to work as a designer with Convair Aircraft in San Diego, eventually taking American citizenship.

My younger brother, Reg, whose twin died shortly after birth, was only age four at the outbreak of the war, but it was not long before he acquired a tin helmet and a mock rifle. Collecting shrapnel fragments of bombs and land mines, and pieces of aircraft, became his hobby, before he started collecting train numbers. Tiring of this, he then took up line fishing, and the family enjoyed many a succulent fish as a result. Reg was one of three siblings to have red hair, but he was very happy with his, and was teased a lot by me for spending so much time in front of the mirror grooming himself. I was little surprised when he took up hairdressing as a career. In later life, his son turned his inherited red hair to his advantage when he found fame as the lead singer in the band, Simply Red.

— FOUR —

A MOVING EXPERIENCE

When my parents first moved into the flat, as newly-weds, it was sufficient for their needs, but as the family grew, so did unemployment, and my father was reluctant to leave it. Work, the pub and his allotment freed him from enduring his waking hours in the overcrowded flat. My mother frequently went to the housing department at the council offices to plead for a council house, or at least to be moved up on the 'list'. She had little or no encouragement from my father, but his complacent attitude only strengthened her determination.

'You are only wasting your time. We've got a roof over our heads and that's it as far as they are concerned,' was his reaction.

Mam was not to be put off, and it was not until Reg's birth in 1935 and the death of his twin, that a tribunal finally granted her a three bedroomed council house. We were all overjoyed, and even Dad had to admit that Mam had pulled it off despite his misgivings.

'It'll mean a higher rent and furniture to be bought, and a further distance from the shipyard,' he grumbled. 'I'll have to get a bike as well, but I suppose we'll manage.'

'Of course we'll manage. How have we managed here? It will be like living in a palace after this.'

It was a sunny Saturday April day when happily, but a little tearfully, we waved goodbye to our friends and neighbours in the Old Barrow flats, and headed across town to our new home bordering on the countryside. Gardens, three reservoirs, a quarry nearby and an adjacent building site for a new estate, held out the excitement of unexplored territory. A cemetery across the road only added to my sense of the unknown.

With my baby brother, Reg, in the pram, my sister Sarah pushing it, my older brother, Alfie, on one side and me clinging on the other, we were the advance party, and probably raised fear in existing residents. Mam and Dad and my sister Lena were coming later in the removal van. My older brothers, Jack and George were at work. As we wheeled the perambulator into the street, a woman's face appeared at a window, grimaced, and put out her tongue at us. Not to be outdone, we made faces back.

'What a nice welcome!' Sarah voiced all our thoughts. 'Glad we're not living next to her.'

I looked at other windows, expecting other faces to appear in hostility, but none did. Perhaps they were all out, I thought, and would show their displeasure when they met us. I did not think that grown-ups put out their tongues at people. It had never happened at Old Barrow.

Our house was at the end of the cul-de-sac, and, as Mam said, it was a palace to us. We immediately felt that we belonged and had come home. We pushed the pram down our own path, feeling very self-conscious, knowing that neighbours' lace curtains were twitching. Sarah had the key and fumbled with it before opening the door. We could not get inside quickly enough to explore. Never had we been in such a large house. Three bedrooms, a bathroom, a living room, a sitting room, and a kitchen, all ours, and awaiting our inspection. We probed, poked and approved, claimed possession of our bedrooms and agreed how lucky we were, our excited voices resounding in the emptiness.

'Have we nothing to eat?' asked Alfie, who was thinner than me and always hungry.

'We've got the baby's bottle and a cabbage,' joked Sarah, picking Reg up from the pram and putting the bottle into his mouth. We had forgotten the baby in our excitement.

In the pram were the remains of dry foods Mam had

given us to bring, flour, sugar, tea, oats, and a cabbage.

'We could cook the cabbage if we had a pan,' said Alf, crestfallen.

'Try it raw, like in a salad,' suggested Sarah.

We pulled the leaves off to taste them. They were tough and bitter and we spat them out.

'I know, we'll play hide and seek,' I said, thinking of all the corners and cupboards for hiding places.

We ran through the rooms, and found unexpected places to hide, until we grew weary of the game, then sat on the floor to wait for the arrival of our parents and, we hoped, food.

On their arrival it did not take long for the sparse furniture to be allocated its appropriate place and it seemed to consolidate our occupancy of the house. In the kitchen, the long wooden table, its top white and worn with daily scrubbing, was waiting for the preparation of our first meal. The grey enamel gas stove, was unusable until Monday when the man from the Gas Board would come to connect it.

In the living room, a chaise longue, a relic from a grandmother I never knew, looked strange, as though it did not belong there. A dining table with barley sugar legs, newly acquired second-hand for £4, stood amidst a scattering of chairs. The treadle Singer sewing machine found its predestined place in the window. The rented Rediffusion radio, a two foot high plywood box in stained mahogany, sat silently in the corner nearest to the only electric socket in the room. A black marble clock, won in a raffle by my father, and much cosseted by him to keep it going, was given its rightful place on the mantlepiece. On his insistence it was kept ten minutes fast, to ensure that we were ahead of time. Of course his theory never held up as we always deducted ten minutes from the time on the clock.

The focal point of the living room was the fireplace, or range, as my father called it. It was constantly blackleaded and burnished by Lena and by being well looked after, gave out as good as it got. As well as the open fire grate, it had a boiler, an oven, a trivet for a kettle or pan, and knobs and handles for mysterious flues. These forever needed either opening or closing, depending on whether the heat was required under the boiler for the hot water, into the room for heating or under the oven for baking. With three or four baking days a week, when round loaves of dough would be resting in front of the fire, the smell of bread baking in the oven enticingly pervading the house added to our sense of well-being.

The coming and going during the day going to work, or school, coming home for midday dinner (never ever was it called lunch) made the living room a place in constant momentum, but in the evenings and at night we sat round the fireplace talking or listening to the Home Service on the radio, only giving up our seats to visitors. Then we children would sit on the floor, listening and absorbing their gossip and opinions, but rarely speaking unless spoken to.

'There is enough furniture for us to get by on,' Dad said, 'Any more will have to wait.'

Paying by hire purchase, getting credit, loans, or mortgages, were not options for my father. That was getting into debt. 'Club' cheques, whereby one paid weekly for an item were borderline, and only used for clothing. Far better, in his view, was to wait until one could afford it, or go without, except at Christmas when Dad drew some tontine money, having contributed every week into it. The sitting room was bereft of furniture, except for a wind-up gramophone, but what did it matter? It would be little used for now. At least there was a bed in each bedroom and chairs in the living room. We had arrived at our predestined place, and we all felt better for it.

— FIVE —

A NEW WORLD

Change was in the air as the fashions of the 1930s took hold, and my sisters made it known that they were decorating the house their way. They stripped the walls of the old beige wallpaper and pasted up bright deco geometric designs. New curtains were made and hung, with cushions to match. Linoleum replaced the old oilcloth. The rag rugs our parents had so laboriously pegged were discarded to be replaced by shop-bought, jazzy-patterned rugs, and the house took on a modern, lighter look. There was change in my sisters too.

At eighteen, Minnie emerged from the chrysalis of puberty to young womanhood with confidence in herself and, sporting slacks, lipstick and a Marcel wave hairstyle with a kiss curl, got a job behind the cocktail bar at the Criterion Hotel, which kept her out until eleven at night. The lipstick was not put on until she was at work, because of Dad's disapproval.

'Do you have to paint yourself like that? Your mother never found it necessary.'

But Minnie persevered and won her independence.

Lena, although five years older, did not go out to work as she was restricted by her disability, but to establish her independence, and to generate an income, she used a Singer sewing machine. She was quick in operating it with her only foot on a treadle, and made children's dresses, which she sold to a retailer. I would take them to the shop in half-dozen lots. If their offer was below the price expected by my sister, I would sigh and look crestfallen and ask for them back. Usually the owner would relent and pay up. I learnt early that if you held out long enough for something you usually got it.

Sarah, in her last year at the Victoria School for Girls, insisted henceforth on being called Sally. She was blossoming out as a dark-haired, vivacious beauty, attracting all the boys and playing one off against the others. Her school was next to mine, and she would unwillingly accompany me.

'Get ready, our Joe, or I'll not take you,' was a familiar cry.

So it was quickly on with my grey flannel short trousers and jacket, and a mile of walking, hopping, and skipping to school, which did not disappoint, and was something to look forward to. Teachers who had time for me, a day of play, games and singing, and new playmates, all heightened my enthusiasm as each day came, but new friends brought new awareness and comparisons.

I noticed that some parents would wait for their children coming out of school, and get into conversation with the teachers. My parents never visited the school, or asked the teacher's name. Most of the children wore shoes, but I wore studded boots. They also wore underpants, which I did not. A further sly revelation was that some had been circumcised, and I had not. A world of differences was opening up to me.

Shops started selling enticing new sweets. Kit Kat, Aero and Mars bars made their first appearance. Wrapped and sliced bread appeared but, as Mam continued to bake her own, we never had any. She said it tasted like cotton wool anyway, but how could she know when she never bought any, and had she tasted cotton wool?

New art deco picture palaces opened up, the Ritz and the Roxy, luxurious and blazoning with neon lights. The Ritz not only had a restaurant but also an electric organ which changed colours as it slowly rose up on the stage, played by an organist resplendent in evening dress.

One day in the playground we saw a plane circling overhead, twisting and turning, with the vapour coming out of it making the word 'Persil' in the sky. Mam said it was a new washing powder, but she would stick to Sunlight soap. Another day, we were all let out of the classrooms to see a giant airship in the sky, with the word 'Hindenburg' on it, and what the teacher said was a swastika. It hovered above our heads, low enough for us to read numbers on it, before flying off towards the shipyard.

The Dixon family at number one bought the first car in the street, a Morris 8, which I always touched when I passed, but there were many more cars seen on the roads, all of them black. I saw workmen putting up the first Belisha beacon crossing in the town, in Abbey Road, and crossed the road twice to see if cars stopped for me. Dad said it was named after some politician.

'Take care when crossing on them beacons. The cars may not always stop,' he warned.

'There's not the horses there were on the roads, and none of the droppings either,' he said, reflecting on his garden.

At home one day when I went to the lavatory, there was a toilet roll hanging. Mam said it was not before time, but I was used to toilet paper at school, so it was not new to me. Before then there had been newspapers cut up into squares by Dad, and hung on a piece of string. Neither the 'News of the World', which usually enlightened my sexual ignorance, nor the 'Daily Herald', a Labour paper, made good toilet paper.

Dad had plenty to do without cutting up newspapers. He gardened, grew vegetables, cut our hair, mended our shoes, and went to work, which did not leave him much time for going to the pub to play dominoes. Mam too, was always busy, with shopping, cooking and washing. Monday was washing day, seemingly always a damp depressing day, usually with stew for dinner. Mam would light the gas boiler in the wash house, boil the washing, rotating it with the dolly legs, then lift it out with wooden tongs, scrub any remaining dirt on the scrubbing board, then rinse it all before putting it through the mangle and hanging it out to dry.

Baking days, on Thursdays and Sundays, were more appreciated. Then, the house was warm and dry, and the enticing smell wafted around the house, with round loaves rising in front of the fire, and plates of currant slices, ginger bread, apple pies or jam tarts cooling on the kitchen table.

1937 was the Coronation year of King George the Sixth, when in common with most other streets, we had a street party. Trestle tables were put up the length of the street, and the street was decorated with Union Jack flags, and red, white and blue ribbons. Everyone brought out chairs and plates of food, and Mam made lots of cakes. We had just sat down to sandwiches, cakes, buns, jelly and custard, when a neighbour, a Mr Hardy, who had a megaphone, and seemed to have taken charge, said that we were to stand up and sing the national anthem first. But Mrs Godwin, who lived next door to him stood up, and said that grace should be said first, so we all sat down again, then Mr Hardy said grace, but he did not look too happy. We all stood up again and sang 'God save our gracious King,' and Mr Hardy looked happier, and then said 'Now sit down, and tuck in.'

An unnecessary invitation, as we were already tucking in and filling ourselves as though we had not eaten for weeks. When the tables were empty, except for a few buns which some of the boys had thrown, we started getting up, but Mr Hardy said to sit and wait and we would be given something. Ladies came round and handed each of us a Coronation mug, and a bag of sweets. Later, the tables were cleared and we started playing games. Mr Hardy brought out a wind-up gramophone and began playing records. Some women danced together, and eventually a few of their husbands joined them, but my parents remained seated. I don't think they ever danced. I had never seen all the neighbours together before, looking so happy enjoying each other's company.

'I wonder if it will ever happen again?' said Dad, but it took a war before it did.

— Six —

PENNIES FROM HEAVEN

First step on the stairs, then the second. Stood on a daddy long legs, twice, and still it flew. So I allowed it its life. It went ahead of me, resting. I poked at it with my finger and it flew on. It was autumn.

'Would you like to go mushrooming in the morning? It looks damp enough.' This was Dad as I made my way upstairs to bed.

Yes, I would like that, but not the getting up at five o'clock, on Dad's insistence, to be earlier than other foragers. Off we would go on our Raleigh bikes, backs straight, pedalling up the road, past the gamekeeper's cottage, to the woods and fields we knew from experience to be the best places. I would scramble into the woods for mushrooms and hazelnuts. The fungi were strange and deadly-looking, inviting in a challenging way, and the hazelnuts were few and had to be searched for amongst the branches and leaves. Only rarely did I fill a pocket. Our knowledge of which fungi were edible did not extend much beyond field mushrooms, so we concentrated on scouring the fields, foraging in grass heavy with dew, looking for the telltale white tops peeping through. Sometimes these would be spotted in the distance, only to reveal puffballs which Dad said were tasteless and not worth taking home. I was sad to see these huge white domes left to decay, and could not resist the occasional kick to see a cloud of spores rise up. Some mornings our foraging would be in vain, but most mornings we would proudly cycle home with the harvest in a tea towel hanging from the handlebars, our appetites enhanced by our early rising and the scents and fresh air of the countryside.

Then the delight of feasting on our bounty. Any of the family who were lucky to be at home joined in a breakfast of aromatic earthy mushrooms fried with bacon, which added to their flavour. Olive oil for culinary use was unheard of. It was only kept in miniature bottles bought from the chemists for softening ear wax.

Free food was a rare find and not to be scoffed at, but many other equally productive activities filled my days, more so if they were moneymaking ones. I had realised early in life that money made the world go round, and I was going to get some of it. A newspaper round was a regular source, but this meant meeting the 6 a.m. mail train to collect the newspapers, taking them to the newsagent, then helping to number and sort them out into bags for street distribution. Most homes had a newspaper delivered and the round had to be completed before going to school, but this was not my only foray into newspaper distribution.

Having delivered the newspapers, each week I would call on the customers and ask if they had any newspapers they were finished with, which usually they were happy to give me. I had a wheelbarrow, knocked together by my Dad, which I could fill with newspapers in a morning's collection. It took a lot of newspapers to fill the wheelbarrow as there were only six or eight pages, due to paper restrictions, and I had to make sure that they were all clean. Then I touted them round the fish and chip shops at a shilling a load. The fish and chip fryers were ready to take all I had collected and I had a regular supply at no cost. Recycling was not a word in common currency then but, in fact, it was an established practice. Bottles for beer and drinks were charged for. Packaging was minimal and bags were reused. Milk came in returnable bottles or one took a jug to the dairy to have it filled. Collecting empty bottles from neighbours, and returning them to the shops for 'money back', as well as running errands, added up the pennies.

The wheelbarrow had other mercenary uses too. I wheeled it around the streets looking for horse droppings which I then shovelled up and got a shilling a load from Dad. It needed a good hosing-out before using it again for newspapers. Dray horses were a common sight on the roads, and following them eventually paid off. Our vegetable crops were well manured.

Pennies and the wheelbarrow came together again when 5th November loomed and another seasonable opportunity arose to turn an honest penny. A straw-stuffed effigy of Guy Fawkes, masked and clothed in rags, would be put into the wheelbarrow and wheeled around the streets. A placard around his neck inviting donations of a 'Penny for the Guy' invariably got a smile and sometimes a penny to be spent on fireworks.

To satisfy my moneymaking disposition I turned to other seasonal opportunities. Carol singing started in the first week in December, usually with my sister Sally accompanying me. First we chose the right street, as some streets paid better than others, then the house. It had to have a cared-for appearance, hopefully reflecting the occupants, and a light on which suggested someone was in. After two choruses of 'O Come all ye Faithful', or 'Silent Night', my finger would be on the doorbell before striking up another carol. Sometimes, but rarely, we were paid off with sixpence which, perhaps mistakenly, we took for appreciation of our singing abilities. Pennies were more usually given, often with the admonishment not to harass the occupants again.

After Christmas and into January and February any fall of snow meant another source of income. Carrying our garden spade we searched out the most prosperous looking houses with drives and knocked on the doors.

'Can we clear your drive, Mrs?' usually met with the affirmative. People didn't mind paying for the service, and usually handed out a sixpence or even a shilling when the job was done. Snowfalls during the night meant an early start before the snow turned to slush and melted away.

Pennies added up, although it took a long time, as there were two hundred and forty to the pound. There were halfpennies and even farthings in circulation. Twopence could be expected as payment when a neighbour asked me to run an errand for them, or in common parlance, a message. It was a welcome supplement to Dad's weekly pocket money handout, now increased to sixpence. Without the convenience of fridges, cars and supermarkets, shopping was a daily necessity. Corner shops were prominent on most street corners, and these, together with the 'Co-op' shops, provided most people's daily needs.

Our nearest corner shop was run by a middle-aged married couple, Mr and Mrs Benson, with the occasional help of their daughter Mavis, a beautiful fair-haired fragile creature in her mid-twenties. The shop was simply a converted front room of a terraced house, with the owners' living quarters at the back. To get into the shop Mr Benson had knocked an opening in the dividing wall allowing access from their living room when the shop bell rang. Unfortunately the height of the opening was so low that, to avoid hitting their heads, it necessitated them stooping with knees bent, to get through. If a customer was already in the shop and being served, one felt a relief on entering the shop that the owners were not put to the inconvenience of having to leave their living room to serve. If there was no customer already in, one felt an apology was called for at disturbing them.

Mrs Benson was small, slight and rather frail, but a pleasant and kindly woman, and eased herself through the aperture without undue difficulty, and indeed with some decorum. Mr Benson, however, was tall, well built and rather irritable and grumpy. If no one was in the shop when I entered, I would wait in anticipation to see who would emerge through the opening, always hoping that it would be Mrs Benson, who would give a welcoming smile. If it was her husband, he would show his displeasure at being disturbed and, no doubt, at having to bend double. His impatience showed even more if they didn't have what I asked for. On the more rare occasions when Mavis came through, it was titillating to see her bent over, always emerging backwards, bottom first, head bowed, with her golden tresses hanging down in front of her partially exposed breast. I was then inclined to apologise for having the effrontery to expect this apparition to condescend to serve me, which she deigned to do with a look of forbearance.

Everything was on shelves behind the counter and waiting to see who would emerge through the opening added anticipation to the shopping experience and gave time to view the shelves for any recent introductions to the limited range. Nothing was priced as the prices were known and rarely changed. Many goods had to be weighed out, and it was not uncommon to arrive home for Mam to exclaim, 'They've given you short weight,' or 'They've added a penny onto that.' Taking something back was a fearful experience. There had to be a sound reason to win the argument which usually ensued.

I soon became something more than the most regular customer of the 'Bensons' when they realised that I had access to a wheeled vehicle, no less than the wheelbarrow my Dad had knocked together for me. Having no transport of their own they paid me sixpence a time to wheel it to the wholesalers in town for a sack of potatoes whenever they had sold out. It became a weekly addition to my Post Office savings account which I held in the next corner shop, a sub-Post Office and bakery combined.

This was run by two spinster sisters, the Misses Hellings. The older sister ran both the Post Office counter and the shop, and was unfailingly patient with every customer, although there was invariably a queue of equally patient people. She was not young, probably mid-fifties, and sighed as she moved from standing at the counter to sitting behind a metal grill, to dispense stamps, postal orders, or saving certificates. She wore a sad expression and it was thought that her one love in life had been killed in the First World War and she had never got over it.

Her sister, the less attractive of the two, baked the bread, cakes and pies, which had to be ordered in advance. She was mainly out of sight, although in between bakes she would idle into the shop, dusted with flour, to have a chat with a customer. She never served in the shop, however long the queue; her sister never allowed her to. She played a subservient role to her sister, but her baking was supreme. My mother did her own baking, but for a change we would buy meat pies, which had to be ordered before 10 a.m. to collect at noon. The pies were delicious thin pastry filled with tasty minced beef. Gravy was given free if a jug was taken, and I had many a swig of it on the way home and to be told on arrival, 'You didn't get much gravy, did you?'

It was at the Co-op where most people did their weekly shopping. There would be eight or ten counter staff taking customers' orders. A bill for the cost, together with the customers' money, would then be put into a small round wooden barrel-shaped box which was operated by a pulley system on wires hanging from the ceiling. The assistant would pull a lever which sent the box along the wire to the cash office. It was returned with the change and a counterfoil, which was then handed over with the goods.

Customers collected a dividend on the purchases which was paid out twice a year in cash. It could amount to several pounds, sometimes the equivalent to a week's wage and was always looked forward to. Usually it was earmarked for a necessary household purchase, but Mam always made sure there was money left for a treat, be it a cinema visit or a café meal. On one 'Divi Day' payout, she took me to McDowells, the best mens' and boys' wear shop in town, to buy me my first new overcoat, a double-breasted light blue belted coat, of my own choosing. Like the blue-eyed boy I felt privileged as I knew it was paid for out of the cherished 'Divi' payout.

Mam never stinted in her concern for all her family, particularly our health. Daily doses of questionable tonics and 'Parishes Chemical Food', an iron supplement, and malt and cod liver oil were regularly administered; hardly necessary with the wholesome meals she cooked, but considered by her to be vital for our health and to 'build us up'. However meagre the housekeeping money, we never went hungry.

— Seven —

A KNOCK ON THE DOOR

Visitors and weekends came together when I was young and started on Friday evenings when pay packets were still hot in the workers' hands. According to my mother, some men handed over the pay packet to their wives intact, but my father took out his own pocket money before handing over his weekly pay packet to Mam and she managed the entire household budget on what was left. I never knew how much he took out and sometimes neither did Mam. She knew what his basic wage was, but occasionally, if he had worked overtime, his wage slip would be missing, which would give rise to the accusation that he didn't want her to know how much he had earned that week. This would create tension between them, but I thought it hard on Dad that he had to resort to deceit to benefit from volunteering to work extra hours, after having laboured all his life to support his family.

Tradesmen who were paid weekly would start arriving at the house on Friday evenings to be head of the queue for payment. First to call was Mr West, the coalman, who made us his last call, in time for tea. He and his mate, hats in hand, leather aprons on their backs, eyes shining out of their black coal-dusted faces, would be invited into the kitchen to sit down and drink their mugs of tea. Momentarily forgetting they were coalmen they would discuss their families with Mam, who always had a sympathetic ear for people's concerns. Then, rising from their chairs, leaving behind a circle of coal dust on the floor, they would confide with a hint of generosity that they had a good load on this week.

'Would it be regular or nutty slack? Six bags or four?'

Coming back, carrying sacks of coal on their backs, they

would tip them out over their heads into the coal hole.

'Count how many they bring in,' Mam would ask me, ever wary of being fooled.

Mam would examine the coal after they left, declaring, 'Lumps are too big', or 'There's a lot of dust in it,' or 'Poor lot this week.' 'You've got to watch them,' she would warn me but despite this she would still welcome them with tea every week.

Although it was only the coalmen who could look forward to tea, all callers were invited in to collect their weekly payments, ready waiting for them on the windowsill. Ten and sixpence for the rent, a shilling for the insurance, two shillings and sixpence for the club money, one and sixpence for the radio, a shilling for the window cleaner. Windows got dirty from the industrial grime and needed cleaning every other week.

The rent woman, her leather bag slung over her neck, oblivious to any fear of assault, never with time to stop and gossip, was straight in and out of the house.

The forever cheery Provident Club man with the false assurance of providing an indispensable service and always with the same loaded question.

'Do you need any additions? I have to ask.'

The Rediffusion man, hand stretched out for money for a radio we never owned but only rented on a weekly payment.

The man from the Pru', on his sit-up-and-beg bicycle, ankles tight with trouser clips, always lingering at the door for a sniff of extra insurance.

'Will that be all?'

'I'm paying enough out,' Mam would retort. 'And I'm not likely to be having any more children.'

At each of our births she had taken out a penny policy payable on death to cover our funeral expenses. She kept them up until we started work when we had the choice of either keeping them on ourselves or having them 'paid up' and getting a pittance on death. Only Jack, the 'faint-hearted', and the eldest son and twenty years older than me, kept his on because, I assumed, he was nearest to cashing it in.

All the collectors came, winter and summer, wet or dry, before the week's pay flowed away on the essentials of food, clothes, Dad's cigarettes, medicines and the doctor's bills, or frittered away on beer and the pictures.

Saturday's visitors were usually friends of my brothers and sisters calling to go out. David, eighteen, tall, fair-haired and handsome, a bosom friend of my brother George, and salivated over by my sisters. He was destined for the navy and sank with the Ark Royal. Tom McGuire, Irish and vociferous, a practical joker, who could make cards disappear. He too died a watery death. Handsome Harry, besotted with my sister Sally; jealous of anyone else's admiring glances and following her like a shadow. Janet, a friend of Minnie's, both sporting kiss curls, berets, and scarlet lipstick, and sharing secrets. Tom, Alf's friend, a gentle and gifted artist, an only child who enjoyed our family life. He went to America and started his own family. I looked up to them all, and aspired to be grown-up like them.

Sundays were when relatives called, when the playing cards were put away as soon as we saw them walking down the path. There was always tea and home-baked cakes to welcome them, but they did not need encouragement. Aunt Lily was everyone's favourite. She was buxom, bright, amusing, a gifted storyteller, and generous, always handing me sixpence on departing. Aunt Lizzie, her sister-in-law, who usually came with her, was fat, and after she had squeezed herself into the most comfortable armchair, had difficulty getting out without assistance, but while she was in it, she held court. She talked loudly, stopping only to gasp for breath, her bosom heaving, and her eyes closed. I was transfixed by her and wondered how long she could talk for with her eyes closed. Her husband, Richard, worshipped her, which I could never understand until I saw a wedding photograph and Aunt Lizzie looked radiant and trim. I am sure that in his mind she had never changed.

Some Sundays I would be out and regret missing the visitors and the gossip which they engaged in, but I had found other things to do. I had made friends with an old couple, a Mr and Mrs Hinchcliffe, who had a garden on the road to the cemetery with a hut from which they sold flowers they had grown. Sunday was the busiest day for visiting the dead, if the weather was fine, and they only opened during the summer when they had flowers to sell.

'Not that many people put flowers on the graves in winter. The dead can wait for better weather', Mr Hinchcliffe said when I asked him if he had considered getting flowers in to sell.

When trade was slow, as it often was, they were happy for me to man the flower stall on my own. They paid me according to how much I had sold, but some Sundays I never sold a bunch and I rarely received more than sixpence, which I could have got from visitors if I had stayed at home, but I enjoyed my first foray into the business of selling and, however modest the return was, I appreciated the trust the owners had in me.

Two other 'Aunts', who were not really related to us at all, but were old friends of my parents, and frequent visitors on Sundays, were sisters, Aunt Helen and Aunt Martha, and they had a secret which they shared with my mother, and, of course, ultimately we all got to know. Helen had had a baby, a boy, before marriage, and rather than face the shame which then existed of having an illegitimate child, she gave the boy to her married sister Martha to bring up. He grew up thinking Martha was his mother, and referred to his real mother as Aunt Helen. I often played with the boy, who was my own age, and promised my mother never to tell him, a promise I kept. At the time, and since, I felt guilt in knowing something so important and fundamental to him, and his being denied that knowledge.

Many other aunts, uncles and cousins visited spasmodically from near and far, some with strange accents and mannerisms; sisters and brothers of my parents who themselves came from large families. Aunt Sarah, my mother's eldest sister, who had married a Catholic, and whose daughter was a nun. Aunt Ginny, on my father's side, whose children kept a monkey in their garden. Uncle Jack who had run a mobile fish and chip van in Workington. Aunt Minnie, who had married a miner from Doncaster and was always in desperate straits and being helped out by parcels of clothing sent by my mother. Aunt Maud, Dad's twin sister, who married into money and owned her own house in Coventry and sent *us* parcels. Over time we all got to know our namesakes and wondered why we had been named after them when we found out that was all we had in common.

— Eight —

JIM AND BEAT

Dad was a twin, born in 1888, and one of eleven children. He recalled to me the day when, as a small child, the family moved from his birthplace in Lincolnshire to Cumbria. His father had already gone there to work, and his mother and the children were to follow. It was at the end of the nineteenth century, and they had never travelled on a train before. Arriving at the station, they boarded the first train, only to be told by a guard that it was a cattle wagon. When their train later arrived they were surprised by the comfort and luxury of the coaches, and were hesitant to get in until the guard reassured them that it was third class and that it was their train. My father told me that when the first steam train entered Nottingham earlier in the century, my namesake, the Reverend Joseph Hucknall, a primitive Methodist minister, led his congregation into the streets 'to pray to God to take this monster from us'.

In his youth Dad had been an apprentice printer, but failed to finish his apprenticeship as he wanted to earn more money. He had met my mother and they had fallen in love. James and Beatrice, known to all as Jim and Beat, married in 1909, when they were both aged twenty-one, and had their first child John, who later was known as Jack, the same year. Five years later at the outbreak of the World War and with two more children, Dad took the King's shilling, joined the Border Regiment, and went to fight in France where he transferred to the Machine Gun Corps. The four years of unrelenting slaughter in the trenches took their toll, and although he was fortunate compared to the many who sacrificed their lives, Mam said he came back a hardened and stricter father who had lost his capacity for emotion.

My mother was born in Whitehaven, a Cumbrian port that in its early years engaged in the sea trade between the Americas, Africa, and other ports in England. She spoke of a grandfather, on her mother's side, who had been a sea captain. Her girlhood was largely spent in helping an elder sister to bring up her nine children, which continued after my mother married, and her sister had died. Despite having children of her own, my mother continued some of the responsibility of bringing up her deceased sister's children, much to the disapproval of my father. I only knew these cousins later as adults and they still showed great affection for my mother, and continued to visit her throughout their lives, despite veiled protestations from my father. I silently shared my father's jealousy of these unsolicited visits as the cousins seemed to have extraordinary claims on my mother's affections which I resented.

Like most homosexual men and boys I was closer to my mother than my father. He showed little outward affection. His fathering was more of a responsibility and necessity, not done grudgingly, but with sternness and strictness and few words. Love he undoubtedly had. He showed it in a practical, enduring, unemotional way. It was by the lack of emotion that his children remembered him. If only he could have hugged his sons, kissed and embraced his daughters, shown the affection which he had for them and his wife, his and our lives would have been lighter and happier.

It would have been too much to expect of a man who had fought in the trenches of the First World War as a machine-gunner. What stories could he have told his children? How he had survived? How many German soldiers had he killed? How many deaths had he witnessed? Not stories to tell your children, and so he kept his silence.

The interwar years of depression and unemployment in Barrow made life a struggle, with little or no state help, but by the mid 1930s the shipyard was building ships again, and Dad had regular employment as a labourer in the boiler shop, often working a shift pattern of two weeks on night shift followed by two weeks on days. How his body, frequently racked with bronchitis and pneumonia, adjusted to this topsy-turvy life was rarely questioned. He accepted it with little complaint. He was of slight build, of fragile health, a very light eater, and also a light sleeper, which, when he was on night shift and sleeping during the day, meant keeping the noise level low in the house. If his sleep was interrupted he could wake up in a bad mood.

'Don't disturb your father!' was a frequent warning from Mam as we tiptoed up the stairs.

Bad moods could have other origins too. Frequently he overstayed his Sunday midday visit to the 'Welcome Inn' pub, where he was an avid dominoes player, and then he was reproached by Mam.

'Your dinner's wasted! One day in the week when you can sit down with us and you are not here!'

The words were wasted too.

'Give up, Beat. I'll not be dictated to.'

I would have the presentiment of a cloud on the horizon and retire to my bedroom to read the latest *Just William* book, borrowed from the library, or go out and catch crickets on the grass bank at the back of the house. The only book we had in the house was *Pilgrim's Progress*, which I thought a very dry book. No one could say how it had arrived in the house, and nobody else had read it.

Mam loved the cinema, particularly if Bette Davies or Joan Crawford was in the film, and expected Dad to accompany her. Unfortunately Dad had little liking for 'the pictures' and only went under protest. Invariably it was at weekends, when Dad had been out for his midday pub visit, and then retired to bed to sleep off the after-effects.

'See if your Dad is awake,' Mam would say, come six

o'clock.

It was not on tiptoes this time when, going up the stairs, I would make as much noise as possible, in the hope of wakening him before having to shake him from his slumber. Usually Dad acquiesced and Mam got her relaxation at the 'pictures'. On summer evenings their preferences coincided and a walk into the country with a pub visit ensured serenity for the weekend.

As a schoolboy during the war I felt relief if my parents reached agreement to go out on a Saturday night, giving Sarah, Alf, Reg and myself the house to ourselves. Alf, always thin and wiry, had an insatiable hunger, and would immediately make for the pantry. If there was no food that could be eaten without being missed by our mother, he resorted to the chip pan which had a wire basket and fat or dripping in the bottom. By carefully lifting out the wire basket, Alf was able to scrape out some fat and adeptly replace the basket with the top layer of fat intact, apparently undisturbed. He then used it to fry bread, which we all loved. Alf was adroit at making cocoa and then adding water to the remainder of the milk, and slicing off pieces of cake, pies or cheese, but never enough for Mam to notice.

Sunday dinners were invariably roasts and when the last remains of the meal were cleared from the table, the tablecloth put away, and there were no relations visiting, the question would be put:

'Who's for cards?'

Newmarket or Rummy were our preferences; games we played for pennies. Pennies could mount up in losses or gains, and an afternoon's play often went on into the evening in trying to retrieve losses. Jack my eldest brother was acknowledged by all to be the meanest in the family and, although he was the highest earner and still living at home, he could not bear to lose at cards, particularly to me, the youngest player. Jack had little empathy with his siblings. He had memories as a boy of begging for food from shipyard workers as they came out of the shipyard gates with their remains of their 'snap', and once being caught by Dad for doing it and being strapped.

Later on when he worked at the shipyard himself he had long periods of unemployment. He frequently reminded me how lucky I was to be born later and not having to endure the poverty he had to when young. He was growing up during the four years Dad was in the First World War, and Mam told me that there had been resentment between them when Dad returned from the war. Dad often referred to him as 'faint-hearted Jack'.

Jack had attracted a number of girl friends, but did not fall in love until the age of thirty-three, when he met Edith, an older divorcee, with two daughters, one of whom suffered from tuberculosis. Divorce carried a stigma with it, and Dad could not countenance a divorced woman as a daughter-in-law. After angry exchanges, Jack moved out of the home, and married Edith. None of the family were invited to the wedding, but eventually wounds were healed and Jack and Edith began visiting.

Edith was a frail thin woman with a sharpness in features and a hardness of character, critical even of Jack, whom she renamed Larry, because he bore a resemblance to Laurence Olivier. She was even more critical of her invalid daughter, Joan, saying she should be working instead of nursing her tuberculosis. Joan died in her late teens, after which there were frequent tearful visits to her grave by her mother taking flowers.

'If only Edith had shown as much sympathy to her daughter when she was alive, she might still be with us,' was Mam's often-stated opinion.

Nevertheless, I felt well disposed towards Aunt Edith, as I called her, and not only because of the sixpences she always gave me. I felt sorry for her as she frequently reminded me that her death was imminent, and her being such a thin frail woman, I would not have been surprised if she had dropped dead in front of me. She often complained to Jack that when she had died, he would quickly find another woman, but in fact he was totally in love with her and put her above everyone.

If I was in need of pocket money I knew a visit to Edith would bring the reward of a sixpence, but I resented her calling me Joey, as we used to have a budgie by that name. After questioning me about what everyone in the family had been doing, she would ask, 'What is your Dad saying about me?' and then before I could think of a tactful reply she answered herself, 'Nothing complimentary, I'll be bound.'

She was right of course and I felt a Judas as I took my sixpence.

— Nine —

CALL ME SPUD

At home, beds, like everything else, were shared. In the nineteen forties, three sisters slept in their own room, all in one bed. Sally, being the youngest, in the middle, the least popular space. Although she had a serene personality, she strongly objected to this arrangement, having endured it all her young life. She was in her early twenties, attractive, with black wavy hair, dark brown eyes, and a rose complexion, and could attract any young man she wished. One, Harry, was obviously in love with her, and plied his troth relentlessly, seeing off all competition. He lived with his widowed mother but, when not at work, spent most of his time at our house. He had proposed several times to Sally. It was a hot summer and she had had enough of sleeping three in a bed and so consented.

Housing was virtually unobtainable for several years after the war, which meant Sally moving in with Harry's mother. Like the proverbial mother-in-law, she made life very difficult for Sally by her demanding ways, and expecting her son to give her precedence over his wife. Harry was placid by nature and had no wish to displease or upset his mother, so early married life was a succession of keeping the peace, at least until the children arrived, and then Sally insisted that they took precedence.

Three in a bed was also necessary for the boys, sometimes four if two of my elder brothers were at home. My oldest brother, Jack, rightly claimed the single bed unless one of us was ill, which left George and Alf, both my seniors, and Reg, my younger brother, and myself sharing the double bed. Fortunately, George, being in the Navy, was rarely at home, and would more likely to be slinging his hammock on board ship. During George's sailing the oceans, initially in merchant ships, he contracted malaria on the Gold Coast and on one shore leave whilst at home he broke out in a fever. This meant the single bed to himself, a coal fire being lit in the bedroom, and nursing by Mam, whilst he suffered hot and cold sweats, weakness and deliriums.

Then he never wanted to put to sea again, but neither did he want to work in the confines of the shipyard, the town's main employer. When he was fit he could not wait to return to the sea. He was cut out to be a sailor, and true to tradition, probably had a girl in every port. We only knew of the ones who sent him letters. Girls from Newfoundland, Sydney and Cape Town were the most persistent letter writers, and he talked of emigrating after the war, if only he could decide on which girl to marry. He had a girlfriend at home, named Beryl, who was a childhood sweetheart. Perhaps it was his experience of the exotic, or maybe Beryl was too nice and predictable a girl to inflame his passion, but the relationship cooled. George could certainly pull the girls, either by looks, or his friendly personality. He had curly black hair, brown eyes which shone with life, a ready smile and a generous and happy disposition.

On one of his shore leaves, having docked in Liverpool and, no doubt having had one too many drinks, he invited a 'girlfriend' home for the weekend. How long he had known her we did not know, but as this was the first time he had ever invited a lady friend home, apart from Beryl, the family's interest was aroused. He had arranged to meet her train and to bring her home by taxi. We waited in anticipation for after all it could be a serious affair. This could be the one.

The taxi drove up to the house, and George got out followed by an amply built, bosomy, blond young woman. She had red shoes and a short jacket to match, with a thin knee-length blue dress. George carried her overnight bag and escorted her down the path to the front door, which was open, awaiting her arrival.

Mam and Dad went forward to greet her.

'Hi, how nice to meet you,' she enthused in a loud voice. 'Call me Spud!'

George was standing behind her, his face red with embarrassment.

'Her name is Murphy. That's why she is known as Spud,' he explained to our parents, who were clearly taken aback by this manifestation.

'Doesn't she have another name?' asked Mam.

George turned to Spud.

'What is your first name?'

'Alice, but who wants to be called Alice? I don't!'

We all stood there, weighing up the audaciousness of Alice, or was it Spud?

Mam regained her composure, and realising she had a guest, invited her to have dinner.

'I'd like to make up first. Where's my room?'

She appeared to have an excess of make-up on already. The little-used sitting room had been converted into a bedroom for her and Mam showed her into it. Dad heatedly turned on George.

'What are you thinking of, bringing a woman like that home? Where did you pick her up? Lime Street?'

George lost some of his colour, but none of his embarrassment.

'She is a good sort when you get to know her.'

'I have no intention of getting to know her, and anyway, how long have you known her? I want her out of here, quickly.'

Dad had Victorian values and was a disciplinarian. He would have banned his daughters using lipstick if they had not made a united stand against him.

Mam intervened, trying to calm the waters.

'You cannot put her out. She's just arrived.'

'She goes first thing in the morning. When I get up, I don't want to see her here. She's damaged goods, a trollop!'

George faced his father, looked as if he was ready to strike him, thought better of it, turned and left the room.

Five minutes later he returned with Spud and they both sat down to their meal, on their own, with Mam waiting on them. Spud ravenously ate all that was put before her and got second helpings, and appeared unaware of the reaction she had created. After the meal, George said they would be going out for the night. We never saw Spud again. George returned next morning, abashed and apologetic, ready to face up to a confrontation with Dad, but Dad's temper had cooled down by then.

'You may have thought of your Mother's feelings before inviting that woman home. What were you thinking of?'

'I'd had a few too many.'

'Then you had better give up drinking.'

Of course George did not take Dad's advice and, after the war, left the Navy to settle down in 'Civvy Street', determined never to work in the shipyard, viewing it as demoralising and restrictive, and tried unsuccessfully to earn a living as a jobbing builder, before finally finding employment with British Rail. He took up with a workmate of our sister Minnie, named Barbara, a rough, robust, vociferous but plain speaking young woman.

'You've chosen a rough diamond there,' was Dad's verdict.

'Yes, but she is a diamond,' acknowledged George.

George and Barbara were well matched, both being diamonds with rough edges, and within the year they married, stayed happily married, and in as many years, produced eight children, four girls and four boys.

— TEN —

IT'S WAR!

All the family were gathered together in the living room waiting in sombre anticipation for the radio announcement, which we had been told to expect. Throughout the country and Empire we knew other families also waited, and on everyone's lips the same question, 'Would it be peace or war?' I was ten years old on that fateful September Sunday in 1939. Old enough to feel the tenseness and gravity of the atmosphere in the room, filled so rarely with the entire family. Young enough to know that whatever it was we were waiting for, it would affect all our tomorrows.

Amidst the calm but ominous words, I heard, 'Consequently this country is at war with Germany,' the solemnity of the words reflected in the voice. The air in the room suddenly became heavy and I felt a sinking feeling in my heart. Dad said, 'Well, that's it, then,' and we realised that nothing would be the same again.

The announcement did not seem to surprise anyone. It certainly did not surprise me; after all, I had been issued with a gas mask at school weeks before, and had practised how to use it. It was hot and restrictive in use and smelled of rubber and I did not like carrying it around in a cardboard box strung around my neck. We were told not to go out without it. We had also taken shelter in the school's cellars as practice for air attacks, and had evacuation drills. I was soon to learn that they were just some of the preparations for war and that there were many more to come.

Nights became darker as all lights were dimmed or blacked out. The street lamppost which had been a focal point at night for meeting friends and playing games around, was now unlit, and the street, like all the other streets, was in darkness. In time, our eyes became accustomed to the dark and shadowy figures looming up ahead. Sandbags were filled and stacked up against public buildings for protection. Windows were either crisscrossed with brown gummed tape to give protection from glass fragments, or boarded up. Silver barrage balloons appeared in the sky, anchored by wires to the ground, and 'manned' by women of the WRAF. Queues formed for Identity Cards, then for food rationing books and clothing coupons, and as the war progressed, queuing became second nature to us.

True to the war aims, democracy reigned in our house. Mam had decided that we would each have our own rations, and be responsible for making them last the week. She apportioned them out each week, putting them into containers marked with our names. This fair sharing of rations applied to sugar, butter, cheese, eggs, and bacon. Rarely did they last out the week. I soon decided to stop putting sugar into my tea, considering it a waste of valuable rations, when instead I could use it to make toffee, usually cinder toffee, or butterscotch, using my butter ration.

Other rationed food items were used for cooking, which was supplemented by unfamiliar wartime introductions, many of them from the USA, such as dried egg powder, milk powder and spam. In addition to ration books, a 'Points' system was introduced, which enabled the purchase of unrationed, but restricted foods. Different items were given 'Points' values and everyone was allocated a number of 'Points', which were like stamps, allowing people the choice of what to use them for.

Wartime recipes were produced by the Ministry of Food, encouraging housewives to use more of the available home-grown food, such as carrots and potatoes. One year when they was an overabundance of carrots, propaganda was put out that eating more carrots helped you to see in the dark, but

I found no difference, and soon got fed up of eating them. The 'National Loaf' was introduced, using more of the husk than in white bread, which was no longer available. Mam used to bake her own bread, and would sieve the bran out of the 'National' flour to get a white loaf. Local councils converted public halls and buildings into 'British Restaurants' on the instigation of the Government to 'nourish the masses', and were very popular as they were cheap and supplemented the food rationing.

Queues would suddenly form in front of food shops of people buying in non-rationed food, despite government warnings not to hoard supplies. Supplies soon petered out, but not the queues. They lasted throughout and beyond the war. People would join them often not knowing what they were queuing for. Many times the supply of whatever it was ran out before you got to the counter. Sometimes the queue was for fruit, perhaps a restricted number of oranges, sometimes only one per customer and I never saw a banana until the war was over.

'Dig For Victory', became almost a war cry, with lawns and flower beds turned over to growing vegetables for the 'Home Front', even in some public parks. Dad had always grown vegetables in the back garden, but now the front lawn was also dug over for growing potatoes.

At school, lessons were interrupted for air raid drills. Young teachers suddenly disappeared into the forces, and older teachers, some out of retirement, replaced them. Large gatherings of people were prohibited. Cinemas were closed, and football matches ceased, but were quickly reinstated because of the public outcry and the need to boost morale. Barbed wire fences went up along stretches of the coastline, most of it inaccessible to the public. Pillboxes were erected along the coast and inland at many road junctions. Posters appeared warning that 'Careless talk costs lives', 'Be like Dad – keep Mum', and 'Walls have ears'.

German invasion of England was the widespread expectation of the Government and the people in 1940. Every family received a letter entitled 'If the Invader Comes: What to do – and how to do it'. It left no uncertainty in the mind of the reader, 'The Germans threaten to invade Great Britain. If they do so they will be driven out by our Navy, our Army and our Air Force'. These were Churchillian words. Preparations for an expected invasion gave way to the terror of air raids. The Germans had routed us at Dunkirk and were massing in northern France. German planes were making bombing raids on London, and were now reaching cities and towns in the north. A German prisoner of war camp was built in the Lake District within a day's walk of Barrow. Would there be escapees to hunt down? A government poster warning that 'Freedom is in Danger – Defend it with all your might'. took on another meaning. It was an exciting time to be an eleven-year-old boy.

— ELEVEN —

THE HOME FRONT

'Churchill got it right,' Dad admitted reluctantly. 'I'll give him that, although I still think he's a warmonger.'

He faced his Doctor who was sounding his chest with a stethoscope. Dad was suffering a severe bronchitis attack, and Mam had insisted on calling in the Doctor. Dad was standing with his back to the fire and with only a singlet on, below which his cock hung, heavy and magnificent in its manhood and I felt a guilty thrill as I gazed at it in admiration. It was the first and only time I saw him in his nakedness.

'You can't have it both ways, Jim,' Doctor Farmer retorted. 'He's the man to lead the country. Anyway, don't exert yourself. I'll give you a sick note. Better stay off work for a week until your breathing gets back to normal.'

Normal life did not extend to many people. Every male between the ages of eighteen and forty became liable for service in the armed forces. Many older men volunteered for the Home Guard or the ARP (Air Raid Patrol), but neither Dad's health nor his night shift work in the shipyard allowed him to. Women took on men's jobs to release men for the services, went into manufacturing munitions, volunteered for the services, or the Women's Land Army. In my family, Alf, five years my senior, joined the Local Defence Volunteers which later became the Home Guard. My older brother, George, transferred from the merchant fleet to the Royal Navy. My older sister, Lena who, until the war had not been considered employable because of her disability, was now given a job with the local defence force. Sally went into munitions, and Minnie, my diminutive middle sister, volunteered for the Women's Land Army. She appeared to grow several inches in stature when she changed into her Land Army uniform, with breeches and a hat similar to a Canadian Mountie's hat, and was sent to a farm in Wiltshire. Considering how frightened of cows she had been as a child, it was brave of her to milk one. After a year of milking and herding cows she transferred to forestry, and was fortunate to be sent to the Lake District, almost a home posting. Alf was designated to an anti-aircraft site on Walney Island overlooking the Irish Sea, which filled the free hours he was not working. He had just started at Vickers Armstrong Naval Construction Works, as an engineering apprentice, and within a week felt proud to have seen Winston Churchill on a tour of the works.

At home, the components for our air-raid shelter had arrived. Having our own family air-raid shelter was an advantage, as most of the civil population were directed to take refuge in communal brick and concrete shelters erected in backstreets and public places, or to cellars converted to shelters. Ours was known as an Anderson shelter, named after the then Home Secretary. They were only available to families in danger areas, providing the householder did not earn more than £250 per annum.

'Give me a hand Joe with these,' asked Dad as he handled the sections of corrugated steel sheeting down from the lorry.

I stacked them up against the wall. The sheets had to be bolted together at the top to form a tunnel, but first we had to dig a deep hole in the garden in which to erect them.

Dad had already marked out the area.

'I'll start digging, and you get the barrow and move the earth to the corner. Pile it up as much as you can,' he said.

As I did what I was told, I felt that I was doing my first bit for the war effort. Dad was digging out the earth faster than I could move it, and getting out of breath.

'How deep are you going?' I asked.

‘Oh, five feet at least. The deeper the better.’

It was exhausting work and Dad’s head was sinking deeper into the hole as he shovelled out the earth. Dad was not a tall man, about five feet six, but suddenly I realised that his head was no longer visible. I peered into the hole and got a fright. Dad was lying stretched out in it, looking as if he was in his own grave.

‘Dad, what’s the matter?’

Panicking, I rushed into the house to get Mam, and when we got back Dad was sitting up.

‘I came over funny. I think I fainted.’

Mam looked shocked, and held up her hands imploringly.

‘Digging a hole is not taking it easy as the Doctor told you to do! Leave it for now. I’m sure that Alf and Joe can finish it.’

We did, the next day, and erected the steel sheeting to form the walls and canopy. Then we covered it over with the earth already dug out. A small access space was left at the front through which we crouched and descended backwards down steps Dad had made. Dad duly recovered from his exertion and later fitted a door into the access space, which he thought necessary as a safety precaution to shield us from blasts. He built bunk beds and coated the inside walls with cork fragments to absorb condensation (an idea he got from working on submarines), and laid a cement floor, with a sump hole, which it was my responsibility to empty whenever it filled up. He was adept at making the shelter as comfortable and as safe as possible, and we were all proud of the result. It was the deepest and best-built shelter in the street.

Nightly air raids now became regular occurrences as the German bombers focused on the local shipbuilding and munitions works. Often we did not wait for the warning siren to sound before we encamped for the night in the shelter. We never changed into nightwear, as it was more practical to wear daytime clothing in case of evacuation or rescue. Mam always insisted on carrying the rent book, ration books, identity cards, insurance policies, birth certificates and any money with her. Bank accounts were the preserve of the well-off, not for us. The weekly wage was always paid in cash, after deductions, in a small brown envelope, which workers usually queued for on a Friday evening. Blankets, food, drinks, an oil lamp, were taken down into the shelter each night. A bag of barley sugars gave us succour through the long, dreary nights when sleep eluded us. Then we may have played cards in the dim light, but more often it was just family chatter or neighbourhood gossip when our neighbours joined us.

For many nights and months, the shelter was not only a place of refuge and protection, but also a centre where families and neighbours came together in mutual support and comfort. Many nights there were twelve people taking shelter. Conversation usually turned on how far or how near the bombing was. We learnt to tell from the noise it made.

'Sounds like the shipyard has caught it' or 'That one was near'. Sounds that you never wanted to hear made you look at one another in apprehension.

One morning, an ARP warden called through the opening.

'Stay in the shelter. There's an unexploded bomb fallen nearby.'

It kept us in the shelter all night and all day, until it was defused, but we had been lucky. If the 'all clear' sounded before day break, we would pack our blankets and belongings and catch an hour or two's sleep in the comfort of our beds. At daybreak word soon got around of where bombs had fallen during the night and Reg and I quickly made for the site to collect any remaining shrapnel. Usually it was the town centre which had been hit; any falling outside of that area we inconsiderately spoke of as strays, although people may have lost their lives.

— TWELVE —

ELEVEN PLUS HALF A CROWN

1940 was not the most propitious year to be sitting the eleven plus examination. All that mattered was the war and how we would survive it. Not that my fate was sealed by my failure to pass the exam. No, the die was cast at infant's school, when the headmistress took me from the hand of my eleven-year-old sister Sarah, asked why my mother had not brought me, and sat me at the back of the class'.

Sitting the eleven plus was a non-event for me anyway. Although it was a moment which defined my future, it passed me by. I was in 'B Stream' and knew that to pass the exam I had to be in Miss Watson's 'A Stream' class. I liked Miss Watson and knew she was the best teacher in the school, even though she only took us for poetry, when she made it come alive. She was a spirited spinster, old enough to have been trained in Victorian values. Her poems had the echoes of empire. Kipling's 'Mandalay', Newbolt's 'Temeraire', Masefield's 'Cargoes'. Poems which conjured up an exotic unknown world. I thought that if I had been in her class I would have passed the exam, but only the better-off children seemed to be in it. She would have helped me, which my form teacher, Mr Singleton, never did. He didn't seem to like boys and just ploughed through the lessons and took no interest in us unless we became rowdy and then he would shout at us.

I had another reason to want to be in Miss Watson's class. To be with Sylvia. I was aware of Sylvia when I first moved into the middle school, or primary, as it is now known. Sylvia was in the same 'B Stream' class and sat with the girls on the other side of the room. She had straw-coloured hair, blue eyes and was always smiling. I was very hesitant in making advances to her, imagining her outside my orbit, until one day I plucked up courage and proffered her some sweets. She hesitatingly accepted and by doing so, for the first time, acknowledged my existence. The next day I made sure that my exit from the school coincided with hers and asked if I could walk home with her.

Once I knew where she lived, my walks to school took on a circuitous route in the hope that I would meet her. It was not long before I started dropping little gifts in sealed envelopes through her letter box. For several weeks the gifts used up all my pocket money, but I was caught in the gossamer web of love. At school, it was sufficient for Sylvia to give me a smile for me to jump through hoops, sail the seas, or soar into the clouds. On the occasions when we found ourselves together in the playground, I was bereft of speech, unable to articulate a simple sentence, but Sylvia would soothe my embarrassment with her reassuring friendliness.

She lived some distance from me and apart from walking her home and seeing and playing with her at school, I never got round to asking her out, although she did invite me into her house once when I met her parents who must have thought me a very dull boy as I was overwhelmed by shyness. Nevertheless we remained good friends until she was moved into Miss Watson's 'A Stream' class for the last year. That did not surprise me as I knew that Sylvia was bright and wanted to go to the grammar school, but it did put a divide between us, and I saw her less often. Then, one day I saw her walking out of school with another boy, and it was then that I first experienced the stinging pain of jealousy, particularly as the boy was very popular and from a rich home. I saw them together several times after this, talking and laughing, and the distance between Sylvia and me seemed to grow. To me, Sylvia had moved onto an exalted plane. Unrequited love floundered, the unacknowledged letter box drops ceased and my pocket money went on more selfish purchases.

This was not my only encounter with undefiled love of the opposite sex but the first, and amazingly, for my age, the most profound, as the emotions it aroused were fresh and inexplicable to me. I saw it as a rejection of me by Sylvia because I was no longer on her level, not because we did not like each other.

I turned the vengeance onto myself and banished all thoughts of passing the eleven plus exam. I did not need to try hard.

The question, 'And what did you do at school today?' was never asked of me by my parents, so why tell them that I had sat an examination and failed?

What if I had passed?

'I've passed the eleven plus for the grammar school!' I would have told everyone.

'The grammar school?' Mam would have questioned in surprise. 'That will mean buying a uniform and new shoes and a lot more besides. Staying on until you are sixteen, as well.'

Dad would think that I was getting above myself, wanting shoes instead of boots. I had told him that I had been to a Primrose League meeting last week and he said, 'What do you want to go that for? It's a Conservative organisation!' He didn't answer when I told him that I went because it was a lecture on India.

'Perhaps it was as well that I never passed,' I thought, 'And so saved my parents a lot of money, but they would never know, because I would not be telling. Anyway, I want to leave school at fourteen and be a telegram boy on a bicycle and wear a pillbox hat. People give you tips when you deliver a telegram, and later, I might get promoted to work behind the counter at the General Post Office. Dad said you got a good pension when you worked for them, but I think he was thinking of himself, as you have to be really old to get a pension, and I don't think I will ever be that old.'

Money, or the lack of it, was a prevalent awareness in my boyhood. Any opportunity to acquire it was not to be missed, but there were, in fact, few such occasions. I never thought of thieving as being one of them.

It was a Saturday morning at home when I noticed it. A half-crown coin lying unclaimed on the table and asking to be picked up. Which is what I did, with a feeling of guilt, but of excitement too. I could buy a lot with two shillings and sixpence, despite sweet rationing and a shortage of everything except carrots.

Having pocketed the coin I then stole out of the house, and called on my friend Alan. I would share it with him. We rode on the buses all round the town, before going to Woolworths to buy notebooks, pencils, and crayons, and finally filled ourselves on pop and cakes until it was all spent.

Dinnertime had been and gone when I arrived home with a heavy conscience. There was foreboding in the air, and I was immediately aware that the half-crown had been missed. It was 'club' money belonging to my sister Minnie, left to be collected by the clubman, and no one had been able to account for its disappearance, until I came home with the explanation apparent on my face.

I immediately sought refuge in the toilet and locked the door. This was the one place in the house where no one could get at me, except that they could remonstrate, and in tears, I eventually surrendered, and came out to meet my punishment. My father was waiting in the kitchen, looking very angry, and brandishing the dreaded strap in his hand. This was a length of leather about two inches wide, cut into four strands, and usually hanging by the fireplace as a deterrent to misbehaviour. On the other side of the fireplace hung a brass toasting fork. It was the second strap my father had made, the first one having 'gone missing', although it was suspected that it had been surreptitiously removed from its hook and buried by one of my brothers. George, who had more familiarity with it than my other brothers, would have been brave enough to have done this, but he never let on.

Despite protestations from my mother and sister Minnie, who was also now in tears, and saying that I could have the half-crown, my father grimly ordered everyone out of the kitchen, closed the door, gripped my wrist, and raising the strap above his head, brought it down on my backside. I swung round him trying to avoid the stings of the thongs as he continued to wield the strap. The strikes on my backside were softened a little by my short grey flannel trousers, but stung when the leather landed behind my knees. I cried out in pain, and in a flood of tears, managed to wrench my wrist away, and again retreated to the toilet. There I remained until my mother's final remonstrations persuaded me to come out. My backside had stopped stinging when I ran upstairs and buried myself under the blankets, shamefaced and averting my eyes from everyone for the rest of the day. I felt that I had let my family down.

It was the first and last time I had a beating from Dad and he made no reference to it afterwards, but then no one else did either. It was as if justice had been done, offence committed, punishment paid, and the slate cleaned. I never thought of paying back the money and was never asked to do so. I had paid the price for the crime.

— THIRTEEN —

RITES OF PASSAGE

'Goodbye Sylvia, goodbye Miss Watson, Mr Singleton and all my friends in the middle school.'

Becoming eleven was not just the time to change schools but was also the defining moment between childhood and adolescence and, for a boy, the age from wearing short trousers to long trousers, itself an embarrassing public statement of achieving puberty. People noticed and called attention to it.

Adults' observations of 'Oh, you've grown up suddenly, haven't you?' would send the blood racing to my face as if I had been caught out on some nefarious crime. Did they know that I was having dreams which gave me an erection and made me come? Did my face show that I could get a hard-on and masturbate? Could they know the thoughts I had in bed which weren't ones I could own up to? Or the sexual arousal from sleeping alongside my brothers and feeling the physical intimacy, not daring to give in to it or give it voice?

Adolescent development was also being defined by my schooling. My failure to pass the eleven plus examination meant continuing my elementary education, and so I was assigned to the elementary Hindpool Central Boys' School. It would be another seven years, in 1947, before secondary education was implemented and the school leaving age increased to fifteen. The inhabitants of the Hindpool district shared a reputation for toughness, hardened by their closeness to the iron and steelworks on which the town had been built. The chimneys emitted obnoxious sulphuric fumes and smoke from the blast furnaces which hung in the air unless the wind from the Irish sea was blowing. The waste slag from the furnaces was carried in wagons and pulled by a little steam train chugging up the ever extending bank of waste along the shoreline, before being tipped out, glowing red hot, and, at night, setting the sky ablaze. I was about to engage with the Hindpool boys for the first time.

Walking to my new school on that first day induced a nervousness and an empty ache in my stomach. The thought that I was only one of many new pupils was some comfort. Knowing that others were suffering too made it more bearable. What would the masters be like? They had a reputation for being strict, and the discipline in the school hard. How would I fit in? I had been at ease in the middle school, with friends and teachers I knew. Now I was starting again, at the bottom, in a strange school with teachers I did not know. But that was for later. The more immediate cause for my apprehension was the feared initiation. I had heard that there was one, but no one seemed to know what to expect, and my older brother, Alf, who had been at the school four years earlier, had not warned me about it, perhaps not wanting to scare me.

The new boys, about thirty of us, were corralled together into the far corner of the playground. The doors to the school were barred by the older boys, who were laughing and taunting us. As the time for the classes drew near these boys formed two facing lines in front of the doors, making a human corridor, which we had to go through to get into the school. To cries of 'Come on you pigs', and with taunts and threats from the older boys, the bravest of the new intake ventured first. They were punched, pummelled, kicked and spat upon as they ran the gauntlet. Several were tripped and kicked.

'Don't let them see you're afraid,' said the boy next to me. 'Make a run through it.'

Mayhem ensued as each of us took a deep breath and ran as fast as the blows and kicks permitted into the safety of the building. Such was our introduction to the school. Whether masters knew of it, or cared, I do not know. There was no playground supervision and most of the teachers were temporary replacements for younger staff teachers who had been called up at the outbreak of the war.

I soon got to know the idiosyncrasies of the teachers. The headmaster, Mr Sawrey, was a stern unbending authoritarian figure, who had been in the First World War. He had deep-set brown eyes under heavy, bushy eyebrows and a chin which appeared to have a hole in it, which I mistakenly took to be a bullet wound. He rarely engaged with individual pupils, appearing too distant except when he took assembly. He obviously derived some satisfaction from endeavouring to instil musical appreciation into us and conducting choral practice by repeatedly rehearsing inappropriate Viennese waltzes. He must have achieved a degree of success as one year we sang the *Blue Danube* as a school choir in the town's Public Hall.

The science teacher, a Mr Thorpe, or 'Thorpy' to the boys, had a habit of unbuttoning a boy's trousers from his braces as the boy stood next to his desk having work marked. If he succeeded, the boy kept his trousers up only by having a hand in his pocket before stumbling back to his own desk. Only once, with much hilarity from the class, did a boy's trousers drop down. A Mr Hodges took us for swimming lessons but these were short lived as a land mine demolished the baths in 1941, putting paid once again to my attempts to learn to swim. I had more familiarity with 'Keasty', a Mr Keast, who, as well as being our Maths and Geography teacher, lived near to me and was our local air raid warden. On chiding me for some error I had made in Maths, Keasty said that I would never get up to my brother Alf's standards, and, of course, I never did. He also took charge of the school allotment, part of the sports ground dug over for the 'Dig for Victory' campaign, which boys who did not play sport were assigned to on sports days. I much preferred working in the allotment to kicking a ball about or fielding at cricket and being bored waiting for a ball to come my way. It was far more interesting and productive to be digging and planting spuds, cabbages and beans, which, if they came up successfully, we were allowed to buy and proudly take home.

Our Art teacher was so small that he stood on a table to instruct us and raising his height had the desired effect of raising our attention. I had the greatest respect for the English and History teacher, Mr Lennon, probably because his subjects had more appeal to me. I thought he was wasting his ability in trying to engage a mostly disinterested class. He was the only teacher whose name was not abbreviated or given a nickname, either out of respect or of unpopularity, although he bore a striking likeness to Humphrey Bogart in appearance and manner of speech.

Lack of supervision outside of lessons prevailed in the school and an established practice after classes on Friday evenings was the 'settling of scores', when differences which had been simmering during the week would be resolved by fisticuffs. Boys would gather in the playground and circle round the two belligerents who fought it out until one of them gave in, bruised and bleeding, or crying and feigning injury to the derision of the onlookers who goaded them on with whoops of encouragement and bravado. Whispers of who would be fighting would pass among the boys in the afternoon and it was not uncommon for several fights to be going on simultaneously after classes.

Of course not all the boys engaged in fights and I certainly avoided doing so by posing no threat to anyone. Most of the time the boys got on well with each other and avoided getting into trouble with authority. Sex was rarely an issue although occasionally boys sitting on the back rows who thought they had cocks worthy of display would show off their erections under their desks, usually to the astonishment of their neighbours.

Friendships were made amongst boys sharing similar interests as in any society and often petered out as interest waned. I was attracted to boys who were different in some aspect from the crowd, or were outsiders. One was an Argentine boy whose father was staying in the town while a ship was being built for the Argentine Navy. His foreignness attracted me and he was the first of many friends from overseas I made later in life. Another friend, Roger, attracted me because he had moved from London and knew a different world from mine. He had one blue eye and one brown eye, which my mother said was a bad sign. Mam was right in this instance as I was to find out. Roger lived with his grandmother and said he had no parents, but never explained why. He had little knowledge of the countryside and I told him that I knew of a secret place which I would share with him.

I had discovered it on my solitary rambles and was captivated by the air of mystery that pervaded it. It was known as the Valley of the Deadly Nightshade, and was surrounded by trees which hid it from the road, and unless you knew it was there, you could miss it. There were the remains of Furness Abbey nearby, which had lain ghostly in the mists of the valley since the dissolution of the monasteries by Henry the Eighth.

It was late evening when I led him along the way and the air was filled with the pungent odour of wild garlic which grew amongst the poisonous purple deadly nightshade. In the quiet and encroaching darkness I felt a thrill in fear of seeing a ghost or an apparition. Surely if such things existed, this was where they would be? We crept silently through the undergrowth of creepers and brambles when we spied a couple embracing against a tree. Roger motioned me to get down which we both did. He then emitted a loud scream and the couple immediately ran as fast as they could, not even looking round. He then pulled out a box of matches from his pocket and said he would start a fire. Ignoring my protestations, which rose more from fear than moral considerations, he got together some dry tinder and put a match to it. We watched it blaze up, but luckily it quickly died out. He made several attempts to start another fire, and got angry when he did not succeed. Roger had not appreciated what the valley offered to the imagination, but I had learnt that some things are best kept secret. One day Roger failed to appear at school and when I went to his home to ask after him, his grandmother told me he had been sent away again.

After the initiation ordeal it was not long before I felt at ease and happy at the school. I soon found new friends, even amongst the Hindpool boys, and engaged in all the activities the school offered, albeit reluctantly with sport. We were encouraged to put on school plays and I loved my first contact with Shakespeare playing Caliban in *The Tempest*. Another boy, Alan Beckwith and I, wrote a radio 'voice only' play, and I spoke the female part, but we were booed by the boys because the curtain stayed closed: an experiment never to be repeated. We were even less popular at 'mind reading', when Alan, dressed in his mother's silk dressing gown and blindfolded by a volunteer from the audience, took to the stage in front of the curtain. I stood behind the curtain having previously made a hole in it to view the audience. Boys were invited to hold up any object they had and I whispered to Alan what it was. He then hesitantly, and feigning a mental struggle, called out what the item was. The deceit lasted until we were again booed off the stage after ten minutes, when I had moved too close behind Alan and my boots were seen projecting from under the curtain.

My happiness in the school was suddenly extinguished when, in my second year, I arrived to find that a bomb had virtually destroyed the nearby railway station and had severely damaged the school which was declared unfit for use. A bit of shrapnel I collected from the debris did alleviate my regrets somewhat but was poor compensation for the loss of a school I had learnt to value. We were transferred to an inferior temporary school building in the town with a huge cooling tower on one side and a brewery on the other and the many improvisations we had to make had a disruptive effect on school activities. Lessons became more haphazard, many facilities were lost and motivation decreased as more teachers disappeared into the armed forces. School life seemed to become secondary to survival.

— FOURTEEN —

EVENINGS WITH MY MOTHER

A bottle of Guinness was my mother's only recourse to alcohol. Sometimes it was brought home by my father from his pub visits, but if he was working nights, I would be asked to go to the off-licence for the beverage. Mother was convinced that it did her good, a claim which we never refuted but which could neither be confirmed. Off-licences then were operated by the brewers and only opened during restricted hours solely for the sale of alcohol. Often they were at the back or on the side of a pub and had a separate entrance.

The nearest off-licences were each a mile away in opposite directions, and it was left for me to decide which to go to. Both were dimly lit, infrequently visited, intimidating places, with rows of bottles of various beers and spirits on the shelves behind the high mahogany counters. In one, I always had to wait for the man to come out of the back room to serve me, despite the doorbell ringing as I entered. Many times I had to go back out and come in again for the bell to ring once more. When I did, the response from the man when he eventually emerged was, 'Just you?' said with a look of disappointment.

Rarely did I meet another customer. I was below the legal age to buy alcohol, but this was never an issue. However, to be on the safe side, I always took a bag to wrap my illicit purchase in case I met a policeman on my way home. Other stouts were available, but my mother only drank Guinness, such was the persuasive power of advertising. 'Guinness Is Good For You', proclaimed the advert, which was the only one she showed any belief in.

Sometimes one off-licence would be out of stock, for it was wartime, and I would then walk the two miles to the other one, as neither was on a bus route. There were no street lights, due to the 'black out', and anyone responsible for showing a light was subject to a fine or, worse, accused of being a conspirator or enemy agent. Even torches had to be dimmed. At bus stops, the government instruction was to shine a torch onto your outstretched hand to stop a bus. My excursions for the bottle of Guinness were always made at night and only for one bottle at a time. Mam thought that one was an indulgence, but that two was an addiction.

On arriving home my mother would turn the radio on to the Light Programme or the Home Service, sit in her chair in front of the fire, stoke up the coals until they were red, and then insert the steel poker into them. While this was heating she would open the bottle and slowly pour out the dark malt elixir, creating a creamy, foaming head. Then the poker would be pulled out of the fire, examined to make sure that the tip was glowing red, and tentatively put into the glass. At the ensuing hissing sound she would remove the poker and, with a look of anticipation, would raise the glass to sip her well-deserved tipple. I watched this regular practice in fascination. To see her look of enjoyment and relaxation made my nocturnal journeys worthwhile. To my questioning of why she used the poker, she said it took the chill off and improved the flavour.

Not all the winter nights were spent indoors over a glass of Guinness, however. Going to the cinemas, or the 'pictures' as we called it, was a weekly habit, and an occasion to dress up and, for a brief time, an escapism from the blackout and deprivations of the war into a world of adventure, drama, comedy, music or romance, with film stars who were larger than life. They were not known as 'stars' without justification. They were created and sustained by Hollywood studios to be the brightest attraction in the universe, with as many worshipers as any religion. Although we favoured the cinemas in the town centre there were in fact nine cinemas to choose from, all thriving throughout the war. Their names evoked the exotic, their origins or their location; the Electric, Gaiety, Palace, Regal, Coliseum, Roxy, Ritz, and the locally named Walney, and Salthouse.

The Ritz had been the last one to open three years before the war and even had a restaurant open for morning coffee, luncheon, tea and supper with waitress service. It was the most luxurious cinema with an art deco interior, and upholstered armchairs to sink into, to experience a comfort only seen on the screen. Usherettes greeted us and led us to our seats like royalty and in the interval served ice cream, until, during the war, it became unavailable. Usually there were two films shown, the main film and a 'B' film, with also a news film. It set the tone for an enjoyable evening outside of our everyday world.

It was in 1939, shortly after the war had been declared, when Mam said that my ever generous Aunt Lily had invited us to see a new film at the Ritz. It was *The Wizard of Oz* and it could not have been released at a more appropriate time. Hearing Judy Garland, sing 'Somewhere Over the Rainbow', for the first time lifted everyone's spirits and gave voice to all our dreams.

A more earthbound entertainment was available at His Majesty's, the local variety theatre, or music hall, to which I would accompany my mother, usually on Monday nights, when seats were half price. Notwithstanding, we would sit in the cheapest seats, the 'Gods', or upper balcony on wooden benches. The theatre was in the old part of the town and had a run-down seediness permeating throughout, but it was also warm and welcoming as we sat reading the myriad of advertisements on the 'safety' screen, waiting for the red plush curtains to go up to reveal the magic of the theatre. Dad was no keener to go to the theatre than to the cinema, but I felt privileged to see some of the entertainers usually only heard on radio come alive. George Robey, Old Mother Riley, Sid Field, Gert and Daisy, comedians, conjurers, men in frocks, women as Burlington Bertie, acrobats, and singers, all doing 'their turn'.

The box office was staffed by a man who used make-up and lipstick and occasionally I would see him walking in the town, brazening out the stares and sniggers of passers-by and think, 'That's a homosexual, that's not me. I can't be one', but I felt very uneasy.

On the way to the theatre my mother would sometimes suggest a stop at the herbalist shop in town. It was a dimly lit place attracting few customers, displaying jars of coloured tonics, dried herbs, purgatives and potions on shelves behind the scrubbed wooden counter and with intoxicating smells of unknown elixirs and brews hanging heavy in the stale air. A wooden bench along the wall added to the feeling of self-denial and temperance and provided spartan comfort to sit and drink our usual threepenny glass of sasparilla, a dark brown sweetened root drink, popular in the area, and considered a tonic by some, including Mam.

Only once did I accompany my mother to her favourite venue, the Spiritualist Church. She was not a religious person, indeed religion was never discussed at home. No spirit tried to make contact with my mother that night, much to her disappointment, but other women there were more accessible. The medium, standing on the platform, her eyes closed, and her voice almost a whisper, asked if there was anyone present who knew of a 'Joan'. Joan had passed over last year and wanted to get in touch with someone there, but no one knew of a deceased Joan.

'Is there a Mildred here?' asked the medium, 'Joan wants to make contact with you.'

A quivering voice spoke up from the back, 'Yes, I'm

Mildred, but I never knew a Joan.'

'Well, you may not have done, but nevertheless, Joan has a message for you. Something about your son. Do you have a son? Is your son getting married?'

'He's courting,' replied Mildred.

'Well, Joan says he will soon get married, and that you will object to it. She wants you to know that they will be very happy together, despite your fears, and you will grow to love his wife as one of your own.'

A muted acceptance and anticipation descended on the audience, all waiting and hoping for someone to make contact with them. A spirit wanted to speak to a Sarah, but there was no Sarah in the hall.

'Perhaps she hasn't come tonight,' ventured the medium.

Someone who had drowned wanted us to know that it had been an accident. Her name was Betty, but no one knew a Betty who had drowned.

I was out of place in this small gathering of old women seeking messages or solace from the dead. My mother's forays into the spirit world rarely gave her any insights into the future as she always hoped, but they seemed to reassure her of an afterlife, despite the protestations and derision of my father.

— FIFTEEN —

TEA IN THE AFTERNOON

My sister Lena was twenty-one when she received a letter from William Berry, the boy who, five years earlier, had sailed to Canada with his brother under the auspices of a Dr Barnardo scheme for orphans. They had been corresponding since his departure in which he had never failed to declare his continuing love. Now he wrote asking her to become engaged to him. Despite the distance between them and not having seen each other for five years, Lena accepted. Shortly afterwards, she received an engagement ring from him with a letter promising his return to England within a year or two, when they would be married.

One, two, three years went by during which William continued to hold out the promise of his return. He wrote that he wanted to save enough to buy a home and have a good start in married life. In the fourth year, in 1939, war was declared, making Atlantic crossings dangerous because of German U-Boat attacks. The marriage was, like so many things in wartime, put on hold 'for the duration' (of the war). Although the war curtailed many people's plans it also created opportunities for others, one of which was to open up more jobs to disabled people.

To Lena, who was then twenty-five, it was a release from her cloistered home life to a responsible paid desk job in the local Defence Force. A big step into the outside world of a wartime workforce which valued and welcomed her. Lena had a natural friendly disposition which soon made her friends, and she quickly adapted to her new environment.

The headquarters of the Defence Force where she worked was located in a requisitioned manor house, a half hour's walk from home for Lena. Her daily walk along the Abbey Road, a pleasant tree-lined street, was noticed by a young naval officer, whose ship was then berthed in Barrow docks and who travelled on the top deck of a bus each day to his hotel on the Abbey Road. From being just an observer he became a silent admirer of this attractive young woman striding out confidently with a walking stick and with an assurance that seemed to make light of her disability.

Harold, for that was his name, was thirty-four years old, and had been in the navy since becoming an artificer apprentice at the age of fifteen. He was now an ethical, unassuming lieutenant commander, who liked nothing more than to exchange his uniform for working overalls or civilian clothing. As his ship was docked in Barrow for several months for a refit, he had full opportunity to wear mufti, and to mingle with the crowd. It also allowed him the luxury of hotel accommodation rather than the restricted confines on board ship. However, there were occasions when, even on shore, uniform was called for, and one such occasion was an official invitation from the local Defence Committee to visit their headquarters. Coincidence, or fate, plays a hand in all our lives, and certainly played a part in Harold's and Lena's. Imagine his surprise when, on being shown around the headquarters, he saw, sitting at her desk, the very young woman who had attracted his attention so often from the bus.

'I know you,' he said to her, smiling.

'I don't think so,' replied Lena in surprise.

'Well, no, you are right. I don't *know* you, but I have seen you before. Many times, in fact.'

'Really, where?'

'Walking up Abbey Road, on your way here.'

'So why didn't I ever see you?'

Lena felt that she was opening a Pandora's Box.

'Ha, that's my secret,' he answered teasingly with a laugh.

Lena felt her pulse racing and knew that her face was colouring. Why was this naval officer showing such an interest in her?

'I'll be back,' he said, again surprising Lena, 'and we can carry on our conversation.'

He resumed his tour with the accompanying director, who had stood back whilst these exchanges were made.

Half an hour later he returned alone to Lena's desk.

'Yes, I will tell you now. I have seen you most days for the past month from the top desk of a bus. Our paths coincide.'

'Well, you do surprise me. Do I stand out?'

Lena immediately regretted having said that. Obviously with her disability and her walking stick, she did stand out.

The conversation lapsed into the routine questions and answers. How long had she been working here? Did she like it? Did she walk all the way? Where from? Eventually Harold asked if they could meet again, perhaps somewhere else.

Lena had infinite questions to ask him but hesitated from doing so. She felt that this was rushing their tentative relationship, but as so often in wartime, immediacy took over.

'Yes, it would be nice to meet again.'

So it was arranged that they would meet the following weekend for afternoon tea.

They fell in love that afternoon. Over the tea and cakes they each discovered that their lives would be incomplete without the other. Lena wrote her last letter to William, explaining that in his continued absence, she had met and fallen in love with someone else and apologetically ending their engagement and returning the ring. William wrote back expressing his disappointment, hoping that she had made the right decision, but that if things didn't turn out right for her, he would still be waiting.

During the next few months Harold and Lena met every

day and lived for each other, but a separation was looming as Harold's ship became ready for sea again. It was 1943 with enemy activity at sea still a formidable force. Before he sailed away, Harold asked Lena to marry him, but to wait until the war was over. In the meantime they would be engaged. No one knew how long the war would continue and Lena wondered if this would be another long engagement but this time she knew that her love would endure the separation, no matter how long.

Harold survived the war and in 1946 they were married, delayed by the war, but finding each other because of it. Lena was thirty-two and Harold was thirty-seven, both of a maturity to know happiness together. Harold remained in the navy but on 'shore' commissions, allowing them the enjoyment of a shared, if postponed, happy married life. They had two children, a girl and a boy, and their future seemed bright but it was not happy ever after; Harold died unexpectedly from cancer twelve years later, leaving Lena a widow at forty-four. Her love did not die with him, and she found the strength to carry on, despite the bitterness she felt at her sudden loss. No other man could replace Harold, not even William, should he still be waiting in Canada.

— SIXTEEN —

IS GOD THERE?

My father showed no interest in religion, and, like sex, never spoke about it. I never questioned him on sex, as I implicitly felt it was a taboo subject, but I did not have the same qualms on religion. When I ventured to ask him if he thought there was a God, he just replied,

'I've no reason to think so.'

'So you are an atheist, then?' I had only recently encountered the word, and wanted to use it.

'If that means I don't believe in God, yes.'

I felt that I had questioned him as far as I dare, and from his attitude, he was not to be drawn into giving his reasons. He had the same closure on politics. When I asked him why he always voted Labour, he said, 'What have I got to conserve?' I could not argue with that.

Mam said that being in the Great War was enough to kill anyone's belief in God, but Dad did not even offer that as a reason. It was probably his denial of religion that induced my mother to seek some meaning in life and to turn to spiritualism.

'And what about you, Mam?' I asked, trying to come to some understanding.

'I've been to enough christenings, deaths, and marriages in church, and churchings,' she added. 'So I suppose I believe.'

'Churchings? What are they?' I asked.

'It's a church visit after having a baby.'

'Did Dad go then?'

'No for goodness sake, only women. Anyway, why are you asking? Your Dad is a good man, and that's what matters.'

It was not long after that exchange, when I answered a knock on the door, opening it to find a black-gowned man in a white clerical collar standing there.

'Is your father or mother in?' he asked.

Mam came to the door.

'I'm visiting all the parishioners to introduce myself to them. I'm Robert Nelson, your new vicar at St Matthews.'

'Oh,' said Mam. 'Do come in.'

I noticed that Dad had retreated from his chair into the kitchen.

The vicar stood by the window.

'Do you come to church?' he asked solemnly.

'Not regularly,' answered Mam, her face reddening. 'I am kept very busy with my family, but I do sometimes go to the spiritualist church.'

'H'm. Perhaps if I leave this leaflet with you? You will be very welcome.'

His looked down on me and smiled.

'Do you go to Sunday school?'

'I used to, when I was younger,' I answered nervously.

'Well, perhaps you would like to come again and join a class?'

When the vicar had gone, Dad came out of hiding in the kitchen.

'I heard him. Gathering his flock! Always touting for recruits!'

'I'm sure he means well,' said Mam, 'Only I'll not be going.'

'Well, I might,' I said, 'To Sunday school again.'

It gave me a mean satisfaction to be at odds with my father on some of his views which seemed to be cast in stone.

'Do as you wish,' said Dad.

Apart from the satisfaction it gave me in challenging Dad's views, I felt a religious curiosity, probably because it had been absent from my life. My parents saw their responsibility to their children as supplying food, clothing and love, and providing we behaved ourselves, kept out of crime, came home before bedtime and attended school regularly we were free to roam at will and to pursue our own interests without constraints from them.

At thirteen I had an awakening sexuality that was not without feelings of guilt, and perceived in the Vicar's invitation a welcoming hand to exorcise these demons. So it was that I found myself sitting in a Sunday school group of other earnest boys and girls, praying and listening to the vicar recounting the Gospels and explaining to us the meanings of the parables. Such was my dedication, that, perceiving a disinterest from my parents, I recounted the stories and parables to my younger brother Reg in bed at night, finishing off by making him recite the Lord's Prayer with me.

Reverend Robert Nelson was a mild mannered, softly spoken, withdrawn and rather humourless man in his early thirties but, in his cassock, and to a boy of my age, a respected figure of authority. I had not been attending Sunday school very long before he suggested that I join his confirmation class. This I eagerly did, without even mentioning it to my parents, as I knew that Dad would not approve, and with several other boys, stayed behind after bible classes, to be instructed into the catechism.

It was some weeks into our instruction, with our anticipated confirmation not far away, when at the end of the lesson I was asked by the vicar to wait in the vestry. I went in alone and for some minutes stood admiring all the different coloured vestments hanging on the rail, curious as to why there should be so many. I became aware of the vicar standing behind me.

'Do you like them?' he asked.

'Yes, but why are there so many colours?'

They seemed to me to be theatrical and at odds with the

sobriety of the church.

'We have different colours for different occasions and services.'

The vicar took a purple one off the rail.

'This is for Lent and Advent. Red is for Palm Sunday and confirmation and the green one is worn on ordinary days. Are you very interested in the church?'

'I don't know much about it,' I said.

'If you are interested, I can tell you all about it. Who knows? You may want to become a priest one day.'

That was something I had never thought of; telegram boy, journalist, yes, but never a priest. Weren't they chosen by God, anyhow?

'I don't think I could,' I answered.

'You never know, Joseph,' he said, smiling at me.

He took my hand as he spoke, and then pressed his fingers into it. I felt nervous and embarrassed, knowing that this should not be happening. With his free hand he touched me in the groin and began to grope me, continuing to smile at me as he did so. My pulse started racing and I pulled away from him in fright and embarrassment. I said that I had to get home and made for the door, and the aisle. He called out after me to come back, but I did not turn. I had to get out and only felt a relief when the church was behind me. On returning home I never told anyone what had happened, avoiding embarrassment and having to tell my father. Anyway, I felt guilt in thinking that I was the cause of the incident.

It was three years before I returned to the church when Robert Nelson officiated at my sister Lena's wedding, during which he remained aloof and kept his eyes averted from me. She later told me that she had found his manner cold and distant, and that he had not added anything to her happiness at the wedding. It surprised her that she had not found him more friendly and she wondered why, being a priest and a married one at that. I thought I knew the reason but I kept my silence.

Reverend Nelson continued in the parish without, to my knowledge, any complaints made against him, until he moved away to become Rector of Liverpool, eventually being appointed Suffragan Bishop of Middleton. I heard him in debate several times on the radio, and wondered if it was the same man I had encountered, as he spoke so rationally and with conviction; not a person hiding behind a mask.

Seventeen years elapsed before I could exonerate him of his abuse of me, when in 1959, I read in a newspaper of him taking his own life in the Craven Hotel, Charing Cross, London, at the age of forty-five. He was found with a blanket over his head in a gas filled bedroom with an eiderdown across the bottom of the door. Several letters were found which clearly showed his intention to take his own life. He was Chaplain to the Queen, and had been attending a conference at Lambeth Palace.

Echoes of the past came back to me as I pictured him in his cassock, a parish priest, standing by the window, confronting Mam and looking down on me, smiling. Had he coveted me then, a young boy? And, as he progressed up the hierarchy of the church, what temptations had he faced and what had he given in to before his conscience brought him to suicide? All I could do was to offer up a silent prayer for him.

— SEVENTEEN —

SITUATIONS WANTED

The aspiration to be a telegram boy was soon forgotten when at fourteen I developed an interest in writing. Having devoured all the *Just William* books available at the public library, I thought I could portray childhood better than the eminent author Richmal Crompton, and set about writing my first book, to which I gave the unambiguous title, *A Splendid Book For Lucky Children*. It was a series of short stories of escapades surprisingly not dissimilar to those of William and his friends.

With the optimism born of ignorance, I sent the handwritten manuscript to the publishers, Messrs George Allen & Unwin Ltd, and after only five anxious days, received an acknowledgement that 'they hope to give an early decision', which further raised my hopes. Eight days later I received their regrets, 'that we do not see our way to make a proposal for its publication', and 'thanking me for giving them the opportunity of seeing the MS'. I was impressed by the politeness and seriousness which they had shown me. It was my first rejection slip, but my interest in writing was awakened. So was Dad's.

'What's all this correspondence you are getting, J. Hucknall Esquire?'

'It's my book I've written.'

'You'll never make a living by writing.'

Thanks Dad, I have a whole list of publishers and I have only tried one, I thought, but kept quiet. I had not considered making a living by it, but Dad had made me think. He had never asked me what I wanted to be when I grew up, but if he had I would not have known what to answer. All I knew was that anything was possible, except the dreaded shipyard, which I definitely knew that I would not be going into.

I would soon be leaving school and thought that perhaps I could go into journalism. Living in a small isolated northern town did not present much opportunity to acquire the skills, let alone get a job. However, there was one local daily newspaper. Its scanty news items were supplemented by a 'Readers Letters' page, to which I had successfully contributed, if only to see my name in print. One on dogs fouling the pavement, and another on the beauty of Furness Abbey ruins.

I wrote to the editor again, but this time to ask if he had a vacancy for a junior reporter. He kindly replied that he had no vacancy, was unlikely to have any in the near future, and anyway did not employ staff below sixteen years of age. At fourteen, even I considered myself too young to leave home to try elsewhere, so out of desperation I put an advertisement in the 'Situations Wanted' column of the newspaper for part-time journalism work. Who I expected to respond to this, in a town bereft of any other journal, I cannot now imagine, but surprisingly it did get one response. It came from the subeditor of the paper, who suggested a meeting at his home.

It was a small rotund man who came to the door, bald with a red face, and a little girl standing behind him. He invited me in, introduced himself, and told the girl to go back to her mother.

'The job is nothing much', he said apologetically. 'And it is only for two hours a week. I would want you to go through the papers I leave you and cut out the items I will have marked and file them into folders. You will come here in the evenings and I'll pay you two shillings an hour.'

I readily agreed to the offer and would eagerly have worked for nothing. An introduction to a real live editor, albeit a subeditor, was reward enough for a fourteen-year-old boy. I volunteered to start the next evening, on the first rung of my journalistic career. I duly arrived to be greeted by his wife who too was small and round with a red face. She showed me into the front room and pointed to a stack of newspapers, handing me a pair of scissors.

'Have you brought the folders?' she asked.

No, I had not.

'Well, you had better clip them together. My husband is working late tonight. Do as many as you can, and I'll ask him to get folders from his office for you for next week. Let yourself out when you have finished.'

She left the room, and I was never to see her again.

The following week, on knocking on the door, the subeditor greeted me, and I followed him into the front room. The pile of newspapers had increased since the previous week, so I saw my job continuing. I sat down on the floor, took the scissors and started at the top of the pile. The subeditor sank into the sofa, half buried himself, and without any preamble, apparently comfortable with my presence, proceeded to read a book.

Not wishing to disturb him, I kept silent, and looked for the red indication marks in the newspapers. There were very few, in fact, and after half an hour, the pile was substantially reduced.

'I've put the folders over there for you. If you are short of a subject, let me know. Now, how about a cup of tea?' he asked.

'Yes please.'

He eased himself up from the depths of his sofa, sighed, and left the room to return ten minutes later with two cups of tea and biscuits. I felt this was a friendly gesture and warmed to him.

'Sit down here,' he said, his hand on the sofa. 'You are working quickly.'

We sat there together drinking our tea and he questioned me lightly about my family and home life. I felt flattered by his apparent interest and the little tension I had first felt changed to a feeling of acceptance and friendliness. He asked what my father did for a living, how big he was, and whether I got on well with him.

'What size shoes does he take?' he asked, much to my surprise.

I did not know, but said that I would find out.

'What size shoe does Dad take?' I asked of Mam when I got home.

'Size seven, but why do you want to know?'

'Oh, I was just wondering', I answered as vaguely as I could.

On my next visit to the subeditor I mentioned the fact, curious as to where it would lead.

'Oh, perfect', he exclaimed, 'I have a pair of almost new brown shoes that size, which are too small for me. He can have them if you don't mind taking them.'

The rest of the evening was as before, tea for two with chat, and then silence prevailing while I reduced the pile of newspapers.

I returned home that night and presented the shoes to my father, repeating the reason for the gift. After trying them on and finding them a perfect fit, he was happy to keep them.

'Never had brown shoes before', he said, 'And of fine leather. Thank him for them, won't you?'

Now that my father had acknowledged my developing friendship, I felt curiously compromised.

The following week the preliminaries followed the now established pattern, the only difference was the smaller pile of newspapers waiting for my scissors, as few had been added since the previous week. With tea and biscuits served, conversation resumed on the sofa, and questions as to what I had been up to since last week. Naturally I was flattered by his interest, until his hand strayed onto my thigh, and then slowly moved up to my crotch and grasped my genitals. I pulled his hand away, stood up, and in embarrassment made for the door. The subeditor apologised for his behaviour, and said he did not know what came over him. I felt affronted and embarrassed. The room seemed to close in on me and I wanted to be outside. I hurriedly left the room, the unfinished newspapers, the subeditor and my burgeoning hopes of a journalistic career.

Why had this happened to me? I had done nothing to provoke him, and yet, like the vicar before him, he had made assumptions of me that I was unable to define. Had they perceived in me an orientation I was afraid to face, that I was physically attracted to men? No school friends had ever confided in me their sexual experiences, but neither had I with them. Sexual activity at school was confined to embarrassing moments in the toilet, and, at the very worst, premature boys showing off their erections below their desks in class.

We maintained a silence on sex at home, although I'm sure that my sisters discussed it amongst themselves, my older brothers never spoke of their experiences to me. It must have been on their minds as, years later, Sally told me that in their pubescent years our brother George had suggested having sex with her as an experiment. She was outraged and would have told Dad if she had not known the consequences George would have suffered at his hands. Our parents, following their own upbringing in Victorian virtues, conceived ten children and maintained silence on the subject. I maintained a silence too, and had only to see my father wearing the brown shoes to recall how he came by them and to wonder what he would say if I told him the full story, but he never did hear it.

— EIGHTEEN —

SUITS YOU SIR!

'Do I have to wear a suit?' asked Dad.

'It would be better if you did. You would make more of an impression,' said Mam.

'I feel it's me going for the interview,'said Dad.

'I wish it was,' I muttered.

This was my first job interview, and my stomach was turning over. After leaving school, I had registered at the Labour Exchange the following week, and looked at the 'Situations Vacant' notice board. Ignoring the manual jobs, and being too young to be an apprentice, the one and only clerical job advertised looked promising. 'Office boy wanted by Pickfords, Removals and Relocations.'

I enquired at the counter if I could apply.

'Grammar school are you?' asked the clerk, knowing only too well that I was not. My details were on my card in front of him.

'No, I'm fourteen,' I said by way of an excuse.

'They need someone with a good hand and a head for figures,' and added with emphasis, 'and fifteen.'

'Well, I would like to apply. I'm fourteen and a half really.'

Despite showing his misgivings, the clerk arranged the interview for the following Monday morning. I lived through the weekend in trepidation, but my father lived through it in dread.

'I think you should go with Joe to his interview,' Mam had suggested.

Dad was unwilling, but in the end, grudgingly agreed, and now we were on our way. Dad in his Sunday blue serge suit, distinctly uncomfortable to be wearing it on a weekday and as usual, not saying much. The depot was located in the old part of the town near the docks. The glass door panel was etched with the word 'Office', and through it I could see a man sitting on a tall stool in front of a high desk. Dad stood behind me and after looking at him for a nod, I knocked.

The man looked up and beckoned us in.

'Mr Hucknall, is it? No need for formalities,' he said, ignoring Dad's proffered hand. 'I've got a paper for your son to fill in. If you will just sit over there,' he continued, motioning to Dad.

I could sense Dad constraining his anger at being treated so discourteously. The man, who had still not introduced himself, handed me a sheet of paper and indicated with his finger for me to sit at an adjoining high desk at which there was another Dickensian high stool. I manoeuvred myself onto it and looked at the paper. My heart sank. The first question was, 'What are the principles of levers?' Then followed questions on how many boxes of defined cubic feet could be got into a defined space and how many cubic feet would be left unused.

At school, my maths had been above average, although as my teacher had said, 'not as good as your brother Alfred.' I attempted the questions but felt my inadequacy. I looked at Dad. He was looking wistfully out of the window.

'Have you finished?' asked the man.

Hesitatingly, I handed him the paper.

'Hmm, do you want more time?'

'No, I don't think so.'

'Well, there is no need to go any further.'

Dad rose, looking relieved, and with a 'thank you', we made our way out.

'Doesn't seem that you got the job,' he said.

'No, I flunked it. He didn't interview me! Anyway, I wouldn't have wanted to work with him.'

'Neither would I,' said Dad.

My next interview for work was in response to a newspaper advertisement for a 'Junior Salesman' at Alexandre, bespoke tailors, part of a group of over 300 shops, but Dad was not to be drawn into accompanying me again. I was greeted very cordially by the manager, who introduced himself as Eric Wilson and proceeded to explain the job to me, the conditions and the starting wage, and then asked me if I was interested. I certainly was, and the following Monday I arrived at the shop feeling very self-conscious. My first day at work!

Eric, as he told me to call him, introduced me to the other assistant salesman, who looked twice my age.

'This is Harry, who will be in charge when I'm not around. Hope you get on well together. Now your first job is to make the tea,' he said escorting me into a back room.

Inside, Eric closed the door.

'Sit down first. I should explain some things to you. Harry is an epileptic. Know what that means? He has fits, and if he has one while I'm around, I will see to him, but if I'm not around, you will have to. Don't be frightened, just roll him onto his back and loosen his tie. Put something under his head, a jacket or a cushion, if you can. He may foam a bit at the mouth, and make incomprehensible sounds, but don't worry. After five minutes he will come to, and not know anything has happened. I'll show you around and tell you your duties after that.'

I was more apprehensive now, but at least I knew what to expect. Eric was a well-dressed, suave, pink-faced, slightly balding, slim man, with an assurance which put me at ease.

'First, I'll show you how to make the tea. It's the most important job you will be doing.'

Tea breaks were as long as they took. Five minutes was enough for me. Harry took ten minutes. Eric read the *Daily Express* and did the crossword and usually took half an hour.

'Now I'll go through the stock with you, Joe, and explain everything you need to know.'

The stock was mainly of bolts of suiting material, stacked in rows on polished wooden shelves, each bolt with a coloured label, detailing the material, a number, the price, and yardage remaining. Red labels denoted old stock which had to be pushed, but meant double commission. Other colours denoted the price range, but £5 was usual for a full suit. It was my duty to brush the top bolts of cloth every morning, dust wherever there was dust, and to sweep the floor whenever necessary.

'Oh, and to serve, if called upon, but that won't be often. I approach customers first, then Harry, then, if we are both busy with customers, you can. It's seniority, you see, and of course, the commission. Anyway, customers are few and far between since the war started, but just in case you are called to serve, I'll run through that with you now. Pretend I'm the customer.'

Eric adopted a hesitating manner, looked around, and sidled up to me. 'I'm getting married next month and I want a new suit. What have you got?'

I had not been in a tailors shop before, but I had seen films and assumed the role of salesman. I picked out a few bolts of suiting, and after attempting to explain the differences to him, asked him his preference. I thought I had made a good attempt at selling, until Eric said, 'Now you be the customer.'

He invited me to sit down, offered me a cigarette, and started talking about weddings and getting married. The bolts of suiting came much later.

'You can hardly talk about marriage, at your age, or offer a cigarette, but perhaps football and a chair? Anyway, you get the point, don't you? As for the suit, customers don't have much choice these days because of the restrictions. No double-breasted jackets, no turn-ups, no wide bottoms, no sleeve buttons, no pleats, no vents, and only Utility cloth, and no suits without coupons! Now tomorrow I will show you how to measure for a suit, but you won't be doing it yet for a while. You need a suit for yourself first. You get fifty percent off your first suit, which you will need to wear for work to look the part. You can pay a little each week from your wages.'

Eric, with what I was to find was his usual tact, had not commented on my well-worn grey trousers and tweed jacket, both of which seemed to have shrunk on my frame. Next day he took the tape measure which he wore round his neck and proceeded to instruct me into the correct art of measuring for a bespoke suit. Back width, arm length, jacket length, all measured precisely and recorded.

'Now, I'll measure you for your trousers. Put your legs slightly apart. Notice how the customer dresses.'

'What do you mean?'

'See how the old man hangs.'

'The old man?'

'Yes, the thing between your legs! Not always noticeable, but if it is, record it on the order form for the cutter to allow for it. Doesn't apply in your case.'

Suddenly, Harry, who had been watching in amusement, fell down in a fit, writhing on the floor and making strange noises. Eric immediately rushed to get a cushion and, putting it under his head, laid him on his back, and then loosened his tie.

'Just leave him now. He'll come round after five minutes.'

Harry was in convulsions and frothing at the mouth. I was glad to have been forewarned, but I still felt frightened and thought how understandable it was in some societies to have suspected the sufferer to be possessed by some devil. After five minutes, Harry regained consciousness, picked himself up, and looking white and shaken, was assisted into the back room by Eric.

In time, I became inured to Harry's fits, and saw to him whether Eric was present or not. Sometimes Harry sensed when a fit was coming on, and would call out or raise his hand, but he only had seconds before the convulsions started. He was exempt from war service on medical grounds, and as I later found out, so was Eric, who had tuberculosis. Eric had periods in a sanatorium, which was the only treatment then available. He had a deceptive appearance of health, and occasionally I was asked why a fit person like him was not in the armed forces.

Eric's tuberculosis worried my mother, who rightly realised that I was being exposed to it, particularly when I announced that I intended staying in the job. After she had met him a few times, however, she succumbed to his charm, and said how lucky I was to have such a nice boss. Fortunately his tuberculosis was not transmitted to me, and as epilepsy was not contagious, I remained in good health.

I was, however, experiencing the trauma of adolescence. Sudden surges of blood to the face showed my embarrassment if anyone mentioned the fact that I was growing taller, or showing signs of hair growth on my face. I knew it was growing in other places too, and changes were occurring there as well. I was ashamed if I had a wet dream, and dreaded the thought that Mam would see any stains on the sheet. I had so many wet dreams that the thought of masturbation rarely arose. I shunned girls and was embarrassed if they showed an attraction for me.

As it was, few females entered the men's tailoring establishment, and those who did were wives who had to coerce their husbands into it. Most men continued to wear suits bought before the war, even long after it, until clothing coupons were finally abolished in 1952. Their wives and daughters were eager recipients of the coupons, which were also often traded or sold on the black market. When I started work in 1943, the clothes ration was thirty six coupons a year per adult, with a suit requiring twenty six or twenty nine, according to the lining.

I could earn extra but illegal money to my wages of two pounds five shillings by trading any surplus coupons which a customer may have, or offering to put turn-ups on trousers, sometimes necessary to clinch the sale. We got round the restriction by adding two inches to the trouser leg measurement, and when the suit arrived from the factory, we changed the straight finish of the trouser into a turn-up. I became adept at this, and charged two shillings and sixpence which went straight into my pocket. No one questioned why so many long legged men ordered their suits from us. Of course, it defeated the whole object of the restriction, which was to minimise the use of material.

In my early days as junior salesman I relished dressing up in a suit and going to work at eight thirty in the morning, when most workers in the town would have put on boiler suits and have been at work since seven o'clock. Going home one evening, I met a school friend coming from his job in the steel works, with his face dirty with grime, wearing a blackened boiler suit and clogs, and I was embarrassed at our contrasting dress, which only a year before had been the same.

With the ease of manner that Eric showed in instructing me, I quickly adapted to the work. There was a lot of satisfaction in assessing a customer, turning an enquiry into a sale, selling a £5 suit to someone who had come in for a £4 suit, seeing the pleasure of a customer on trying on his new suit and at the end of the week, collecting the commission. It was a pleasant working environment with little pressure from the head office in Leeds. A supervisor would visit us occasionally and fill in a report form, but with Eric in charge there was little to go wrong, but after my second year, Eric's tuberculosis got worse and his periods off work became prolonged.

At sixteen I was taking on increased responsibility although Harry was ostensibly in charge when Eric was absent, but this only made his fits more frequent. The work was not onerous and I was happy in the job, but we were both uplifted whenever Eric returned. I saw the prospect of a career continuing after my National Service. I was into my third year when Eric had a prolonged stay at the sanatorium, from which he never returned. The tuberculosis killed him at age forty-seven. A new manager was sent from Leeds, and he was not going to be advised by a seventeen-year-old boy. He had served in the army, the war was over, and the government had decreed that all employers were obliged to re-employ previous employees, after their war service. Thousands of returning ex-servicemen were resuming their pre-war jobs, and later arrivals were being sacked to make room for them. My own National Service was looming up and if the company had kept me on until then, they would have been obliged to re-employ me after my service. I was given a week's notice and an ex-army veteran was reinstated into my job. I wrote a letter of protest to the managing director but to no avail. Suddenly, the prospect of National Service, which until now I had faced with apprehension, held out a welcoming hand.

— NINETEEN —

ARMY INDUCTION

It was January 1947, at the age of eighteen, when I began eight weeks of 'Basic Training' as an army conscript, and reported to Fulwood Barracks in Preston. Victorian, devoid of heating or hot water, four bleak blocks of brick buildings all facing the parade ground, with latrines and washrooms outside. It was the worst winter on record, with heavy snow falls, chaos on the roads and railways, and a serious shortage of fuel.

'Grab a shovel and fill that wagon' was the first command from our corporal, pointing to a mountain of coal. Our first training lesson, do as you are told, and don't ask questions.

A week of shovelling coal was followed by a regime of learning to march, to parade, burrow into holes, leap through hedges, shoot a rifle, and bayonet a bag of straw, accompanied by the appropriate screams. My life had changed, from having freedom of choice and being accountable to myself, I was now a uniformed disciplined soldier, able to repeat my allotted service number, 19143185, when frequently asked to do so, to salute an officer on sight, to march in step, not to shrink when barked at, to shower in cold water at 6.30 a.m. and to know the King's Regulations.

The shock of being involuntarily thrust into regimentation and a communal existence was heightened by the gnawing pain of homesickness. It was not just a state of mind, of loss or attachment, but a physical ache seemingly weighing heavy in the pit of the stomach. Occasional glimpses of civilian life outside the barracks, seeing people going about their normal lives, increased the pain I felt. Only by deliberately dismissing any thoughts of home and family was I able to get through the training period.

Finally came the interview with the assessment officer.

'And what does your father do?' asked the lieutenant, looking over my head.

'He works in a shipyard, sir.'

'Doing what?'

He put the question with a look of total disinterest.

'He's a labourer.'

I had now got his attention. He gave me a withering look.

'And you left school at fourteen?'

Obviously he did not have me down as officer material.

'Yes, sir.'

Why did he require confirmation of this? Did not most boys leave school at fourteen?

'Do you play any sports?' he asked wearily.

'Not really.'

He looked at me balefully; obviously he found his job as personnel assessment officer tedious, and beneath his dignity in having to interview recalcitrant recruits. Or was he just wishing to get back to the officers' mess? Three minutes and he had made his assessment, and with a wave of his hand, and muttering something about the Catering Corp, dismissed me.

After the eight weeks of subjugation in the Victorian barracks, I was 'posted' to the Army Catering Corps Training Centre at Aldershot, for twelve weeks' training to be a cook. It was the practice to assign recruits in batches to fill any deficiencies in establishment numbers. If five hundred cooks were needed, five hundred recruits were allocated to fill the gap, and, as a conscript, I was told that I had to accept the decision.

I had no interest in food beyond satisfying my own appetite and the thought of wasting two years slopping about in army kitchens gave me the courage to challenge the decision. In the meantime I had to go along with the training, given by a diminutive Scottish sergeant, whose constant advice was 'wait for the blue haze.' As I sweated over the hot stove, with trays of liver, sausages or steaks waiting to be dropped into hot fat, I looked in vain for the blue haze to rise. Too late and the oil started smoking and spluttering. Too early and the meat just lay silently in the fat.

I could have held a piping bag all day, squeezing out icing or pyramids of mashed potatoes. There seemed to be an art in that, and I took some pride in making gallons of porridge, soups and tea. In time, I think I would have made a passable army cook. The competition was not great, but I was determined to leave the slop sinks, and hot ovens, and opt for anything outside the kitchen, even the infantry.

To everyone's amazement and after two interviews, my request for reclassification was accepted, and I was sent to a holding unit in Bielefeld, West Germany, to await another posting. After the militaristic discipline of Aldershot, and its blanket of khaki uniformity, the German ex SS German barracks was akin to a Butlin's holiday camp, with a swimming pool, a splendid NAAFI, and the newest cinema in the BAOR (British Army of the Rhine). Best of all, I was given a desk job in Administration, next to the office of the OC (Officer Commanding). Between his door and my desk there was a desk occupied by his daughter, Rosemary, a buxom friendly girl of my own age, who very helpfully guided me into my duties. Other than from her, I received no training, although my job was maintaining records of personnel awaiting posting, and issuing transit instructions to their new postings. The decisions were made by the OC by the simple expedient of taking the name from the top of the list. I am sure that many a square peg landed up in a round hole, and vice versa, but the procedure was never questioned. The maximum stay in the camp was four weeks before a posting was made and another recruit was sent off into the unknown.

By my second week I had ingratiated myself sufficiently with the OC's daughter for her to ask me to get her a few items on the black market, which was rampant then in Germany, as little worth having was otherwise available. Cigarettes were the accepted currency and being then a non-smoker I had all my cigarette rations at my disposal. One of the items she asked me to get, and which cost me five cigarettes, was a pair of sunspecs, which she immediately put on and kept on, even in the office.

Her father would occasionally come out of his office to have a word with her, and when he saw the sunglasses, asked her where she got them from. She said that I had bought them. He gave me a jaundiced look, but said nothing. Understandably he was very protective of his daughter, one of the few officers' daughters loose in a motley mix of Scots, Irish and English soldiers, like myself awaiting postings. Unbeknown to him Rosemary and I had been outside the camp area together, and one weekend at her instigation, visited Belsen, which, two years after liberation, had been cleaned of the debris. Walking amongst the mass graves and remaining foundations of the burnt huts, knowing the inhumanity which they represented, did not arouse any romantic feelings that weekend, but even without the unease they engendered, there was no romance, only friendship.

Women, their availability or not, and sex, either the lack or the experience of it, dominated any conversation amongst soldiers. Sex was easily available but did not attract me. I knew that I was more attracted to men than to women, but would have been ashamed to have admitted it, and sex with another man would have been a criminal act, leading to court martial and imprisonment. One had only to step outside the camp gates to be confronted with a fräulein willing to supplement her meagre living standards by selling sexual favours. If a soldier's principles held fast against taking advantage of the flourishing black market in sex as well as articles, or if he was faithful to a wife or girlfriend, (no one had 'partners' in those days except solicitors) he would very likely be further put off sex by the films we were paraded to watch weekly showing the symptoms and horrible effects of venereal disease. Most soldiers were too scared of the consequences to take the risk, and together with the reputed bromide in the tea, it kept their sexual desire suppressed, although few admitted it.

Two weeks into my desk job and I was escorting Rosemary into town and her father's withering looks towards me intensified. I knew that my posting was imminent. It was handed to me, exceptionally by him, with a look of disdain, and the sparse comment, 'Report tomorrow. You are in the RASC.' That night was happily spent on spit and polish and removing my Army Catering Corps insignia and replacing it with the RASC (Royal Army Service Corps), with a feeling of elation of having won my first battle with authority against all the odds.

— TWENTY —

MY CONSCRIPT YEARS

True to orders, I was transported next day to my new posting, 511 Supply Platoon, a Royal Army Service Corp (RASC) supply depot, in Mülheim-Ruhr, West Germany. Somehow or other, I was never sure how, I had qualified as a clerk. The only training I had received was from Rosemary, the OC's daughter, but I was not complaining. It was better than being in the cookhouse. The job description was a little intimidating: 'Pay clerk and administrative duties, and in addition, in charge of the unit canteen'. I would have to learn on the job.

The Platoon's purpose was to receive incoming food supplies, mainly from Holland and the UK and to allocate and distribute them to Army Units in the BAOR (British Army of the Rhine). We were a working unit with a purposeful role, which left the recruits little time to brood about their loss of home or family. The OC was a Captain Holman, a modest undemanding fatherly figure, weary from the war he had fought in, and looking forward to his retirement. Under him were two conscript subalterns, each eager to outdo the other in justifying their rank by ordering unnecessary drill parades, rifle drills, and equipment inspections, none of which contributed to the working schedule. Much to their chagrin they got little support from the OC. A sergeant and two corporals, each war veterans, also showed little enthusiasm for drill practice as they were waiting for their demob. The largely manual work was done by about twenty 'other ranks' assisted by a dedicated German labour force.

I was not left in doubt for long whether I would fit in or

not, before my duties took over. The sergeant may not have been a stickler for discipline but he was for administration of records and accounts. Fortunately he was prepared to instruct me too. Not without humour, he had a dry Scottish wit which went with his indulgence for the duty free whisky. In addition to my office duties, I was responsible for the unit canteen, keeping stock and giving out weekly rations of cigarettes, beer and alcohol, and selling sundry items. I opened up the canteen at midday for one hour, and again in the evening, and rebuffed any demands to extend these hours, although I did occasionally oblige if asked nicely. This opportunity of bestowing favours to other soldiers was made even more manifest as I was also responsible for documenting and issuing leave passes, and getting interviews for soldiers with the OC. Consequently I was treated with circumspection, if not deference, by all the ranks, despite being a lowly private.

But it was not long before the OC called me into his office.

'I think your position of responsibility, which you have taken on ...' he said, pausing and looking at me curiously, '... warrants you being promoted,' and handed me two stripes. I celebrated that night, after stitching them on.

I was beginning to enjoy the Army. There was no feeling of homesickness now, no questioning of Army discipline, no comparison with civilian life. The unit's personnel replaced the role of the family, and I comfortably fitted into it.

When off duty, evening entertainment was usually a night of drinking and talking in the makeshift mess, and when conversation subsided, a soldier might break into song. 'She's a Lassie from Lancashire', or 'Just a Song at Twilight', got everyone joining in the chorus. If the drinks ran out, the cry would go up for me to open up the canteen and drinking would be resumed. It was not uncommon for soldiers to be carried to their beds, stripped and tucked in by less inebriated drinkers. I had the pleasure of being carried on

1915 Dad & Mam with Jack, Betty & Lena, Ch. 8

1923 Uncle Jack's Mobile Fish 'n' Chips Van, Ch. 7

The Buildings, tenament flats where all my eight siblings and I were born, Ch. 1

1930 Barrow from a shipyard crane. Vickers Armstrong was the town's main employer, building ships and armaments.

c. 1920 Abbey Road. Barrow's main street, Ch. 15

1936 Hindenburg Airship on reconnaissance
over Barrow, Ch. 5

1948 Mam & Dad after 40 years of marriage
and still smiling, Ch. 8

1942 Age thirteen in front of an air raid shelter, Ch. 13

My Four Sisters, Betty, Sally, Minnie & Lena.

1940 In Sunday best with Reg.

1943 Family group exc. Betty and Alf.
(Joe top R.H. corner)

1946 Lena & Harold on their wedding day, Ch. 15

c.1930 Dalton Rd Barrow, Ch. 22
(Woolworths 3*d*. & 6*d*. L.H. side)

1950 Driver Johnnie Jackson & Tommy,
the drayhorse, Ch. 22

1950 Shipyard workers leaving on the five o'clock whistle.

1947 Conscription Platoon, Fulwood Barracks, Preston.
(Joe 2nd row centre), Ch. 19

1948 A posting to the Supply Depot, Müllheim-Ruhr, West Germany, Ch. 20

1948 511 Supply Platoon, Royal Army Service Corp, Ch. 20

1951 Best man at Alf & Yvonne's wedding, Ch. 3

1951 Woolworth trainee manager (R.H. end), Ch. 22

1952 A 'No Fly Holiday', Ch. 24
It never got off the ground!

1936 Hull Woolworth Staff, Ch. 26

1957 Morley Woolworth Staff, Ch. 27

1957 Coach trip from Morley to London, Ch. 27

1957 Woolworth Head Office, Ch. 28

1976 John & Kelly at Christmas, Ch. 37

1985 A champagne send-off from Woolworths.

1986 Mick (Simply Red) with cousins, (centre back).

2003 Reg & Mick on a night out.

1987 Best Man in Jakarta with Theo
and his parents, Ch. 38

1987 Jakarta – in a becak, Ch. 38

1998 With Ramon in Spain, Ch. 39

several occasions, but to my regret, the pleasure did not extend to intimacy. They were an honest, good natured and reliable group, as well integrated as a family, despite coming from different backgrounds and with fascinating accents. Robbo, a Scouse to his bones, brash, witty, humorous and no one's inferior, usually led the singing. Bennett, a small, defiant, promiscuous youth from Truro, had discovered sex early in life and was determined to have his fill. He claimed he could charm any woman into bed, and I did not doubt it. Carter was a sharp-witted Cockney, who took exceptional pride in his turn-out, folding his trousers carefully to get the crease right, and to keep it in by rubbing soap on, before putting them under the mattress every night.

Dave, an aspiring boxer, with a soft Hampshire drawl, was handsome, lithe, outspoken, with a maturity that belied his years. He had been a runaway as a boy, beaten by his father, with a mother he described as 'having a tongue of fire.' I fell for Dave, and although our friendship bonded, his sexual attraction to me was muted. This was unsurprising, as the regulations, as well as the law, forbade any sexual liaison between men. Never in conversation, or in ribaldry, did I ever hear homosexuality raised. Boxing had never before held any interest for me, but to be with Dave, I accompanied him to his fights and readily acted as his second, waiting in his corner to rub him down between rounds. Sadly for me, that was as far as our intimacy got and added to my self-denial of my true sexual orientation.

Off duty, soldiers were now free to fraternise with the local population, and most of them did, with the women. There was only one of our group who was married with a wife in the UK as we were all young recruits. He was a very homesick lance corporal, who lived each day as one less towards demob and being with his wife and only child again. Most of the other soldiers settled into serious relationships with fräuleins. We had four German female staff working in the office, Gertrude, Rica, Paula and Eve, two of whom, Gertrude and Paula, were engaged to Army men. They were all happy, delightful women, glad that their war was over, and that they had jobs with the occupying forces, which provided them with pay and a meagre midday meal. Food and jobs were still scarce for the civilian population, most of whom were impoverished, destitute, or homeless as a result of the war.

I was attracted to Eve, our German translator, who was my own age. We soon discovered shared interests in English literature and poetry. She was serious, well-informed, intelligent and attractive, very much an Anglophile and, I soon found out, a pleasure to be with. We started going on walks together, but we both felt constrained by an older German friend of hers, Fred, who also worked at the unit, and who took it upon himself to be her chaperone. I was never sure where Fred came into her life. Was he a family friend, or a jealous suitor for Eva's affection? His companionship, however worthy, seemed to embarrass her, but she was too polite to confront him about it. Regardless of Fred, I was unsure of my own predilection towards her sex other than knowing that Dave's physique attracted me more than Eve's. Dave was a bigger part of my life, my thoughts, and my dreams.

Wartime years as a boy, confronted by government posters warning of the dangers of casual sex and venereal disease, followed by army indoctrination and films of its consequences, inhibited any sexual desire with women I might have had. An even more formidable suppressant was the MO (Medical Officer), a female Captain Prendergast, of the Army Medical Corp, who was with the nearby Scottish regiment, the Gordon Highlanders, which we were attached to for any medical treatment. Captain Prendergast was the scourge of the regiment and as tough as old boots. Her tongue-lashings of recalcitrant sick applicants were as feared as much as her diagnosis. This kept the numbers going sick very low, but it also inhibited those with serious problems from reporting.

'You don't go to her even if you've got the clap,' I overheard one soldier say to another.

'*Particularly* if you've got it,' said the other.

Syphilis and gonorrhoea – or the clap as it was known – were the dread of the promiscuous soldier, and, in addition to their serious health consequences, it was a chargeable offence to contract a venereal disease, unless previous precautions had been taken and reported on the daily register. A soldier having sexual intercourse was required to enter the fact on the register on his return to barracks. If he failed to do so and contracted venereal disease he could be court martialled.

On one visit to the regiment, I saw a line-up of Gordon Highlanders, reporting for medical examination, ordered by Captain Prendergast to lift up their kilts, while she passed along the line examining their genitalia. It confirmed my conviction that the kilted regiments viewed underpants as an unnecessary hindrance, or a garment for the effete, and reminded me of my schooldays without them.

The Germans looked to us more as protectors against the hated Russian Army than as an occupying force, and this was reinforced during the Berlin blockade in 1948. There was an expectation that our conscript service period of two years would be extended because of the belligerency of the Russians, but because of the success of the Berlin airlift, the situation was defused and my discharge was imminent. I had done my two year service, had found it fulfilling, experienced living in another country, received an exemplary testimonial, and had thoroughly enjoyed army life. I was ready for my demob party, but first I had one more thing to do.

I had access to personnel records of my unit. This gave me the unique opportunity to look up my own records, which included the initial assessment of me by the personnel assessment officer on my enrolment. I remembered myself, two years previous, nervous, anxious, and unhappy. I looked at his handwriting, just a scrawl, and unsurprisingly, only four words.

'Lacks colour and ambition.'

Reading those words, I felt the weight of arbitrary judgment crushing my youth, my happiness and my future. His analysis was not me. It was not part of me. I removed the document and, with a feeling of retribution, put a match to it.

— Twenty-One —

TWO SISTERS

I was back home on my demobilisation, or demob leave, as it was known and, although appreciating once again the comforts of home, I was already missing the camaraderie and sustenance of army life. I felt at the crossroads, uncertain of what I wanted or where to go. But in the euphoric post-war period, opportunities were opening up and, with the extending of the school leaving age from fourteen to fifteen, there was an increased demand for school teachers. I thought it could be a rewarding career if I could get a place at a teacher training college and possibly qualify for a grant. My hopes were short-lived as I soon found that without the minimum qualification of matriculation, the road was barred.

I had to look elsewhere and discovered that business administration courses were being held under the auspices of Manchester University. Teaching was a profession, and business was not considered to be, but even though the entry requirements were less demanding, I think that it was only my enthusiasm which got me accepted. A bigger hurdle was getting a grant, for which I had to face an interviewing panel. Of the three men on the panel, it was the old wizened one in the middle who looked at me with contempt over his pince-nez spectacles, and asked the questions.

'What does your father do?' 'Does he have a bank account?' 'Does he own his own house?' 'Why did you not go to a grammar school?' 'What can you contribute?'

His expression did not change with my answers and it was with surprise and relief that, after the interview, I received a letter advising me that I would be paid a grant for the twelve month course held in Manchester.

I had always had great affection for my two eldest sisters, Beatrice and Lena, but none more so than now, as they both lived in the area. Beatrice, who now wanted to be known as Betty, in Manchester and Lena in nearby Bury, although there was surprisingly little communication between them at the time. They had been close until the war, when travel became more restricted, and exchanging visits decreased, because of rationing and bombing. Each was absorbed in their own world but they both offered me accommodation. I decided that I would have the best of both and stay six months with each of them. The first six months to be with Betty who lived in a small Victorian terraced house in Chorlton-on-Medlock, which after Moss Side, was the most deprived area of the city. In her first days in Manchester she had become seduced by the charms of a young man named George, a small Glaswegian with big ideas and, pre-war, a supporter of Oswald Mosley and the fascists. After a brief courtship, and much to the despair of our parents, she married him.

Now, with five young daughters, and with none of his ideas having born fruit, George was a self-employed window cleaner earning a somewhat erratic income. Nevertheless his self-confidence was exceeded only by his boastfulness and his propensity to drink, both which were nurtured by his loud aggressive Glaswegian mother, who lived nearby and could instil fear into any man's heart.

George had a disruptive kind of nervous energy but when sober he would appear to be solicitous and considerate. He shook my hand with enthusiasm.

'Welcome into the family. Make yourself at home.'

Whatever faults I was to discover in him, meanness was not one of them. Like his mother, being seen to be generous boosted his ego. When his mother had first visited my parents she brought with her a big tin of Cadbury's chocolate biscuits which, as children, greatly impressed us. Disillusion came later when, after a night out, she came home drunk, much to my parents' consternation and, after an argument, berated her son. I kept my distance from her when I came to live in Manchester.

Despite having five young daughters in the house, room was made for me. The children were happy to have an uncle living with them, and I seemed to have restored the family connection that my sister had missed. I soon realised that she was in an unhappy marriage, but her pride kept her from admitting it to our parents. She was very defensive about her husband and even now was in denial about his behaviour, which was at times aggressive and threatening. Only vestiges of love and my sister's pride had kept the marriage together.

The children were often in fear of their father when he came home less than sober, and with good cause. His eldest child, Elizabeth, excelled at school, and had achieved a place in the High School for Girls. Despite her home life, she was a bright happy confident child, one that any other father would have been proud of. Instead, her father was jealous of her and on one occasion showed his animosity by burning her school books. My sister often had to defend her children from his violence, despite his professed love for them, and would rather take the violence upon herself to protect them. Who knows in what circumstances a child is conceived other than the two people who conceive it? Whether in love or lust, willingly or otherwise, a sixth child was on the way.

I tried not to get involved with George's disruptive behaviour, as I did not want to get between a husband and wife. My sister and even her children went out of their way to hide the truth from me. George was careful never to be physically abusive in my or anyone else's presence, only alternating between being argumentative or ingratiating, but I was fully aware of the atmosphere when he was at home. It seemed that my sister was trapped in a marriage she would be better out of, but was unwilling to admit to it. Conditions in the area had improved little since Victorian times, with seemingly a pub on every street corner. The house was overrun by mice which would scurry around the floor as soon as it was dusk, and keeping it clean and bringing up the children, making their clothes and taking in sewing, was as much as my sister could do. My two pounds fifty shillings a week contribution to my board and lodgings was a welcome help to the household budget, but it was not for long. I was three months into my agreed six-month stay, but now with Betty's pregnancy advanced and the pressure on her we agreed that it would be better if I moved to my sister Lena's home.

The contrast between the two sisters' lives had to be experienced. Lena was in a happy loving marriage, with a lovely curly haired one-year-old daughter, Margaret, and the comforts of a suburban semi-detached house in an attractive area. Her husband, Harold, was away during the week on Admiralty work and was assured that my presence would mitigate his absence to some degree. I was the beneficiary of his and my sister's kindness and hospitality, and I happily stayed with them until I finished the business course.

Harold was a teetotaller and a vegetarian but did not impose his abstinence onto me or my sister, except at their wedding, when no wine was served, much to my father's disgust. Harold was a modest man, considerate but taciturn by nature, with firm moral principles, who kept his emotions bottled up and was undemonstrative in his affection to both his wife and child, probably due to his early naval training and discipline.

Harold had an only sister, May, who lived nearby with her husband, Jim, and had no children. She claimed that she was unable to have children, but Lena suspected that she did not want the experience of childbirth. Although she liked to think that the world revolved round her – and her husband took no pains to persuade her otherwise – May loved Margaret and became overtly possessive of the child, even, at one time suggesting adoption of her. Lena was understandably outraged at this and, when Harold tried to excuse his sister's possessiveness, it caused the only friction I ever knew of between them.

May and Jim were in the fortunate – and for 1949, exceptional – position of owning a car, which enabled them to take Margaret on outings, sometimes with Lena, but many times on their own. Often, Lena was under pressure from May's pleading and blandishments. I did not endear myself to her as she rightly saw me as a confidant of my sister. Also, it visibly upset her if she saw me playing with Margaret or wheeling her out in her pram to the nearby park, which I often did. Her attitude to me was cool and condescending.

With little contact between my two sisters, but with me as the go-between, they were not kept in the dark. Lena had no liking for Betty's husband, but refrained from coming between them, and Betty was, I think, ashamed of her circumstances. Betty gave birth to a boy, called him George at her husband's insistence, and asked me to be his godfather. Betty's husband's behaviour was soothed for a while following the birth, but it was not long before it erupted again. On a visit home to our parents, I confirmed to them that their worst fears were justified, and that all Betty wanted was to get away from her husband.

Only my parents and my younger brother Reg were living at home in Barrow, so they were able to offer accommodation to Betty and her family, and without hesitation, agreed to do so. I conveyed the news to my sister and with only their clothing and a few personal possessions, they left their Manchester home and moved in. The children were overjoyed with their new environment and the absence of their father. There were only two unhappy people: George, the deserted husband, and my brother Reg, whose pre-eminence in the household was immediately displaced by five girls and a baby. It was an experience he never forgot, as he had got used to having our parents to himself since I had left home in 1947. Eventually, Betty got a home of her own, but by then, Reg too had left home to join the air force.

George followed his family to Barrow and made several attempts to see Betty and the children, but as none of them wanted to see him, he was warned off by another brother-in-law, Harry, whose physical confrontation with him ensured his hasty retreat back to Manchester and my sister's ultimate divorce from him.

Despite the family traumas, my year at the Manchester College of Commerce, in the Class of 1949, progressed and I felt that I had entered a world of the privileged. From having left school at fourteen I was now sitting with grammar school educated young men and ex-army officers and holding my own against them, but more than that, I felt the privilege of access to further education, and receiving state support. Amongst the small class of twelve, I was also the only one to have gone to an elementary school and to have had a job, both facts which I shamefacedly kept to myself.

I would not have missed a lecture for the world. The lecturers were from the university, industry or commerce, except a barrister who entertained us with stories of the Bar, and got our sympathy when he told us about his financial predicament. Having paid over £4000 for his barrister's training, and after years studying the law, he had to wash dishes in a restaurant to live, while he did his twelve months unpaid pupillage, and was now having to lecture because the income from his briefs was so erratic and unpredictable. He said he could not afford to get married, and when I noticed a hole in the sole of his shoe, I believed him. Suddenly the world of the professionals took on a new light and a business career looked even more rewarding.

Our studies were in economics, business law, statistics, and psychology, interspersed with visits to factories, all very revealing and interesting to me. Silk weaving in

Macclesfield, hatters in Denton, wall paper manufacturers in Darwen, cotton mills, sweet factories, engineering works, clothing workshops throughout Manchester; all busy and productive and employing loyal workers who found us as curious as visitors as we found them.

The course came to an end and I was given a Diploma in Business Administration. The year had been intellectually stimulating and had widened my horizons and knowledge. The grant, of course, also came to an end, so now I had to put what I had learnt to practical use and get a job. The factory visits were looked upon as possible job prospects for us to take up, but none did lead to job offers for any of us. One student decided to go into his family funeral business, another into the family contracting firm, and a third emigrated to Canada. The others were as unsure as I was. We all said our goodbyes after a pub celebration to which the barrister was invited as a non-paying guest, at which he regaled us with more humorous legal stories. I hope that he eventually got many briefs to lift him from his poverty.

Rather than live off the benevolence of my sister and brother-in-law, and with my meagre savings, I decided to go back home to Barrow and make my job applications from there. I was twenty-one with a new phase of my life before me.

— TWENTY-TWO —

A CHANCE MEETING

Arriving home, I felt that I had turned back the clock a year and I was still at the crossroads, looking for a sign of where to go, an indication of what to do. I saw no prospects in my home town, and consequently perused the vacancy columns in the *Daily Telegraph*. The Hong Kong police force was recruiting but it smacked of another 'occupying force' with echoes of empire, which, indeed in 1950 we still had, but was, I decided, not for me. 'Trader' in West Africa did appeal and I got as far as an interview in Manchester and then the offer of the job which was selling textiles to merchants on the Ivory Coast. Indeed they were very keen for me to accept as soon as possible.

Selling goods to trading posts in Africa and buying produce to export had echoes of *Prester John*, an adventure story for boys by John Buchan and my favourite reading as a boy, but their eagerness for me to accept the job raised doubts. My brother George, who had been to the Congo and contracted malaria and ever since had suffered bouts of fever, was against my going, as was my father. I took their advice. I was not adventurous enough, or perhaps too cautious? A job in social services was a possibility. Perhaps this was more me. It offered a graduated career ladder, a job for life and a pension. Dad always said whatever job I got, to make sure it had a pension at the end of it.

Whilst I was deliberating I called on my friend Andy, a popular and gregarious young man whose father was landlord at the Crystal Palace Hotel, except it was not a hotel, but a pub. Usually I would join Andy and his sisters upstairs in the family's living room, but this day he was helping his father behind the bar. It was lunchtime, and Andy asked me to have a drink and introduced me to an elderly man, a business type, at the bar.

'This is Mr Marriot, the Woolworths manager.'

My conversation with the manager centred on our army experiences and despite our age differences and the fact that he had been a captain, we struck a chord with each other. On learning that I was as yet without a job, he told me of the career opportunities in the Company and said if I was interested, to let him know. We shook hands and finishing his beer, he left. I was impressed by his apparent intelligence and discernment.

Andy's father came up to me.

'You know that man is the highest paid man in the town and one of the nicest.'

At home, I considered the two possible alternatives that were opening up to me and the consequences of a decision. Was my future to be in social services, on a modest salary, but living at home and enjoying family life? Or was it to be the competitive world of business, profit motivated, well-paid, but moving from town to town? It was a decision that would determine the rest of my life. The next day I went to see the store manager.

If I expected to be engaged with alacrity I was mistaken, instead I faced discouragement. Managers and executives, from the chairman down, all started with sweeping the floor and I was warned there were many rungs on the ladder to be climbed, and as many to fall off. The Company expected full dedication. Moving between stores meant disruption to any family life. In fact, it was preferred if I stayed single. Besides, salaries of trainee managers meant one could not afford to get married. If I still wished to be considered, an interview could be arranged with the area manager. I did, and it was. The area manager had an affable, open manner, reiterated all the disadvantages I had already heard and told me to go home and think about it.

'It's blood and gold,' he said. 'Nothing in between. Look at our storefronts. That's what the colours stand for.'

Woolworths then was the biggest name on the high street. Supermarkets had not evolved. The Company had more stores than any other retailer and was expanding. It was more profitable than Marks and Spencer and employed more staff. Managers were well-paid on a percentage of store profits with promotion dependent on producing increased profit each year. It had a career structure based on achievement. It had a pension scheme. To me, there were plenty of incentives to go for, and I welcomed the challenge and was accepted.

I was offered a start in my local store at four pounds ten shillings a week and, like all managerial entrants, began on the lowest rung of the ladder, in the stockroom. Putting on a khaki overall, I was immediately thrust into unloading the horse-drawn dray, pulled from the railway station by Tommy, a cart horse, and Johnnie Jackson, its driver, both well known in the town from the 1940s. Cartons, crates, sacks, rolls, boxes and bundles of the thousands of items Woolworths sold all had to be manhandled from the street to the stockroom on the first floor using a lift operated by pulling it up on ropes.

Every night and whenever necessary during the day, I would sweep the sales floor and scrape off the chewing gum. The last job on Saturday nights was to spread oil onto the wooden floor with a squeegee to preserve it and the first job on Monday mornings was to spread feldspar and sawdust over it to soak the oil up and prevent people slipping on the surface. The smell of the oil lingered all week and mixed with the smell of gas from the emergency gas lights, the smells of sweets, slab cake, soaps, scents, cosmetics, shoe leather, paint, moth balls, candles, fertilizers, together with the body smells of the throng of customers, gave the stores an aroma which was identifiable and unique to Woolworths.

In charge of all these stockroom operations was a long

serving, diminutive, bespectacled and spirited spinster with a stinging tongue, named Flo. Relishing her small measure of authority, she cajoled or coerced everyone to get the jobs done. Through long service and dedication, Flo had worked her way up from the counters, via supervisor, to stockroom manageress. Not, it might be thought, a very high climb, but to Flo, it was reward enough; the Salvation Army being the main prop in her life. Considering their small remuneration, the largely female staff in the store showed surprising loyalty to the company and did their jobs with good humour and a certain team spirit.

Initially Flo showed some resentment to me.

'You are just passing through, aren't you, onto higher things?' she taunted, with some sarcasm.

Flo had started in the store as a school leaver when the company's advertising slogan was 'Nothing Over Sixpence' and would stay until her retirement at sixty. She had done all the jobs, worked for many managers, seen many changes, was respected by all, and had the ear of the store manager. I insinuated myself with Flo, flattered her with my adherence to her authority, and humoured her when she was out of sorts. She opened up to me, telling me of her love for her dead father, her invalid aged mother, her work with the Salvation Army, her war years on night watch on the roof of the store, and of the many store managers she had seen pass through, some of whom she had enjoyed working for and some she would not want to see again.

Her eyes lit up when she told me of her role as the store's Father Christmas before the war when the store would be so crowded that a 'one way' system had to be introduced, when each year she would make up boxes of small toys and sweets, wrapped in either pink or blue tissue paper, put them into a sack, and, standing on a platform, hand down the 'gifts' to eager expectant children, in exchange for sixpence. She relived her memories, insignificant to outsiders, but highlights in her life.

'I was the only Father Christmas in town,' she said proudly.

And then my thoughts turned back to the boyhood day when I clutched a sixpence in my hand before deciding to hand it over in exchange for a blue wrapped box and my disappointment on opening it. A few sweets, a tin toy car and a rubber ball did not add up to sixpence or live up to my expectations, and confirmed my suspicion that the eager little woman wearing glasses was not the real Father Christmas anyway.

— TWENTY-THREE —

BESIDE THE SEASIDE

Flo's prediction that I was only 'passing through' came to be realised sooner than she or I expected. After three months under her tutelage it was deemed by management that I should move up a rung of the ladder. The system of payment to store managers necessitated them keeping staff numbers and wages as low as possible, thereby, so it was held, maximizing the profit on which they were paid. The inference was made to me by the manager that I was an 'extra' on the payroll and by moving me on, he benefited by the reduction of four pounds ten shillings from his weekly wage bill.

I was to report to the seaside resort of Southport for the summer season. In the 1950s, mass overseas tourism did not exist. Butlin's holiday camps prospered, and all of Britain's seaside towns were enjoying a boom time. In Southport trains arrived at weekends full of Lancashire millworkers determined to enjoy their annual week's holiday, having saved up all year to do so, mostly through works holiday clubs. On Monday mornings, they descended on Woolworths to buy any forgotten holiday items and postcards to send home. On Fridays they returned to buy presents and sticks of rock to take home. If it rained they crowded in for shelter, queued for the café, bought plastic raincoats, more postcards and presents and, in unaccustomed idleness, patiently waited for the rain to stop. In sunny weather they came early to buy their sandwiches, sun creams, bathing hats, goggles and flippers, buckets and spades, and having filled their bags, headed for the beach.

As a trainee manager in Southport, my weekly salary was increased by £2, including a seaside allowance, and I was allocated four departments to supervise and stock. Most of my 'on the job' training was given by the counter staff who could be relied upon to correct me, perhaps all too readily, if I went wrong. I was to discover that company loyalty was embedded in the firm, from counter staff upwards, and had began with the founding of the Company by Frank Winfield Woolworth in the USA and continued with his first British store in Liverpool in 1909, when the slogan changed from 5 & 10 cents Stores to *3d.* & *6d.* Stores. The majority of the staff were female, mostly unmarried, and looked to the firm for their security. Long-serving staff usually held supervisory roles, and although ninety percent of all employees were female, none were in store management or more senior positions. This was accepted without question, and surprisingly did not diminish the loyalty.

I soon found that the deputy manager in Southport took a more active part in running the store than the manager, when he called me to one side.

'Be careful how you treat Miss Bushby on haberdashery, and what you say to her. It all goes back to the boss. She's his mistress.'

Then added, 'Keep an eye on that blonde girl on sweets. She's on the make.

'And look out for shoplifters. Don't do anything, just report them to me and I'll take care of them.'

'Taking care of them' was something he enjoyed, and was a euphemism for interrogating the suspect in a cubbyhole under the stairs. If they were male and young, and showed no repentance, the interrogation included a few body blows, with threats of worse if they were seen again in the store. Women shoplifters who admitted guilt, and most did when apprehended, were let off with threats of police action if they were caught again. He made the culprits pay for the goods, whether they wanted them or not.

It was March when I arrived, so the summer season had

not got under way. I headed for one of the many streets of boarding houses and guest houses. All had 'Vacancy' signs up and looked very much alike, distinguishable only by their extravagantly exotic names, Bel-Air, Mon Repose, Dream Haven, Belvedere, and leaving much to the imagination. I opted for 'Llanfair' because I had visited the town during youth-hostelling in Snowdonia and rang the bell. Mrs Jones kept the boarding house with the help of her husband and two teenage daughters. She was a round, matronly, pink-faced woman, very welcoming, and showed me a large front room upstairs.

'I have this room available for now.'

'I'll be here for the season, at least,' I said.

She looked me over.

'Well, I will let you have the room at five shillings less than I charge weeklies,' and as an afterthought added, 'You will have to change to a smaller room when the season gets going as I charge more then, and I shall want this room for theatricals anyway.'

'I understand,' I said, or thought I did.

A month later, when I was paying Mrs Jones, she said, 'Oh, I've let your room for next week, and want you to move to the second floor at the back. My theatricals are coming. My husband will move your belongings whilst you are at work.'

I had the feeling of being in transit, but was not unhappy with the arrangement. The room had a skylight through which I could put my head and view the beach. The season was underway and Southport was livening up with visitors arriving in coaches and trains. Few people then had cars. Boarding houses were turning over their signs to 'No Vacancies'.

I encountered a number of visitors on the stairs coming and going, mainly Welsh, and also two of the mysterious theatricals, there for the season. One, a magician, under the appropriated name of Zvengali, who introduced himself to me as James, was of small stature, with a twirly moustache, and hair so black it could only be dyed. He talked almost in a whisper in a lilting voice, which I thought denoted a Welsh background, so I asked him if he was Welsh.

'Yes. With Jones for a name, how could I be any other?' he said with a smile. 'James Jones.'

'So the landlady is Welsh too, is she?' I enquired, as I had not thought of her being Welsh, despite her name.

'No, but her husband is. He's my brother.'

Not having met the husband, all I could say was 'Oh', whilst I pondered on the implications of a Welsh wizard named James Jones, billed as Zvengali, with a brother running a bed and breakfast.

Another theatrical was more reticent and, no doubt, with good reason. He was a very young Roger Moore, who was escorting Dorothy Squires at the time. Miss Squires, as the landlady referred to her, surprisingly was staying there, despite topping the bill at Southport, and being one of the most popular singing stars of the decade. I assumed there must have been a Welsh connection. I only met her on the staircase, although I did see Roger knocking on her door a few times. Roger was struggling to pursue his acting career, but was better known for modeling for advertisements, one being for knitwear, which earned him the nickname 'The Big Knit.' In conversation with him, I discovered that he too had done his national service in the Royal Army Service Corps in Germany, also in a supply depot, but as a captain, not a corporal. I also learned that Dorothy's first job was behind the counter at her local Woolworths in Wales.

I had only been in the attic room two weeks when again I was confronted by an apologetic Mrs Jones.

'We've had to move you to the bathroom on the first floor as we have let your room. My husband has put a mattress base over the bath, and with a mattress on top, it's just like a bed. You'll have a key to your room of course. Everyone will have to use the second floor bathroom.'

At my look of surprise and annoyance, she added, 'I am having to turn people away. You will have your own room back after the season.'

Mrs Jones was not an unkindly woman. She probably thought she was doing me a favour in putting all her other guests at an inconvenience, besides which, she was likely getting double the rate I paid for the room. The Jones family themselves had migrated to their wartime brick shelter in the backyard to free up valuable rooms in the house. Would I next be asked to join them, I wondered? They were beginning to treat me as one of the family.

'No, I don't think I could stay in a bathroom. I will for tonight, but I'll be looking for another place tomorrow,' I said, feeling ungrateful.

Mrs Jones looked crestfallen.

'It may not be for long.'

I was disturbed several times during the night by visitors trying to use the bathroom, who obviously thought I was taking too long over my ablutions, and had to get up several times to answer persistent knocking.

The next day, on recounting my predicament to staff at the store, one girl said that she had an aunt who was looking for a lodger, and offered to introduce me. Without any misgivings, the aunt, a Mrs Appleby, gave me 'the run of the house', as she called it. It was in Ainsdale, a residential part of Southport, and Mrs Appleby emerged, not as a landlady, but a welcoming, kind, and considerate friend. Despite her many qualities, her husband had left her for another woman, but presumably to salve his conscience he visited his wife every Friday evening with a bag of groceries and goodies. Rationing was still on, but he 'had connections'. As his wife was trying to slim, I was the main beneficiary of his atonement, and had a very comfortable home with Mrs Appleby, which regrettably came to an end with the summer season.

— Twenty-Four —

ENTREPRENEURS

During the season at the Southport store I made friends with Harold Ainsworth, another trainee manager, who was of my age, single, debonair and sophisticated, and an accomplished horse rider. He prevailed upon me to take riding lessons and often accompanied me on Sunday morning rides on the Southport sands. He was also an accomplished dancer. He had an easy charm with everyone, particularly women, and encouraged me to accompany him to Saturday night dances at the Floral Hall. To avoid looking a fool on the dance floor, ballroom dance steps had to be learnt, and Harold undertook my tuition. With the store closed at night and the cleaners departed, we had the floor to ourselves. Woolworths had its own record label then called Embassy Records so, putting on the appropriate music, I followed behind Harold, emulating his steps to the quickstep and foxtrot. Then, with an arm around each other, and me following his steps, we were soon waltzing between the counters.

My sexual predilection was ambivalent, and although I had no sexual desire for Harold, or Harold for me, neither had I for the women I hesitatingly asked for a dance at the Floral Hall. To admit to feelings of affection for another man was to be open to abuse and ridicule. Life was much easier to live in the closet. The choice was to be lampooned and ostracised or to feign interest in the opposite sex. Not a difficult choice with homosexual practice a criminal offence.

I could exchange banter about sex and women with other colleagues when necessary, but never felt comfortable doing so. Homosexuality would occasionally be mentioned, but only in derision or referring to incidents in the store. Two men masturbating in the café toilets, caught in the act, who in their haste, had not locked the door. Two pairs of feet observed in a cubicle by Harold, who then filled a bucket of water and poured it over them from the next cubicle. There were also the effeminate, or transgender habitués of the cosmetic counter, smearing the 'Outdoor Girl' lipsticks onto the backs of their hands before choosing, buying depilatory gloves by the dozen, sniffing at the 'Evening In Paris' bottles, whilst often trying to conceal one in their hand, and laughing in my face on their way out.

The millworkers' trains brought all manner of persuasions, with some letting their hair down and living their true identity without the constraints of convention. Young men and women, freed from the restrictions of work for a week, looking for romance or hoping to meet that special person; others just out for a good time. They all eventually found a need to call in at Woolworths if only for its familiarity. Even Judy Garland, who was top of the bill at the Liverpool Empire, made a visit to the cosmetic counter with her manager until the crowds got too much for her and she hastily departed.

My platonic friendship with Harold was sealed when, at the end of the summer season, we were both instructed to report to the Carlisle store. Arriving there, each with our fibre suitcases holding all our possessions, we began looking for accommodation. As none of the store staff could recommend any, we made an unfortunate choice from adverts in the local newspaper. Cost determined that we shared a bedroom; not just a room, but also a bed. This did not raise an eyebrow amongst the staff nor sexual desire in either of us, and with a landlady devoid of imagination, neither was it an issue with her.

Mrs Mossop, our landlady, was a virtual harridan, who refused to heat the house and kept the electricity off at the mains in the cellar until it was dark, while blaming it on the power cuts. Food rationing was still on, and our ration books were kept and used by Mrs Mossop to provide the breakfast and evening meals. One egg a week per person did not go very far, but a good cook could do wonders with spam, dried egg powder, corned beef, and the previously unheard of fish called snook. Unfortunately, Mrs Mossop was not a good cook. The house was gloomy and the atmosphere depressing, reflecting her character, so Harold and I soon decided to move.

Mrs Mossop's reaction was to demand a month's notice, which had not been part of our agreement.

'A week's notice,' we conceded, adding, 'against our will.'

'Well, I'll not give you your ration books then,' she said, playing what she thought was her trump card.

We packed our suitcases, handed her the remaining week's rent, and asked for our ration books.

'No. You shan't have them until the month is out,' she told us in retaliation.

'Then we will go to the police,' we threatened, and left.

Next morning on arriving at the store, we found Mrs Mossop at the doors, with our ration books in her hand.

'There you are then. I haven't slept all night,' she said and, with a tearful look, thrust the books into our hands, crying, 'I hope you're satisfied, and I don't want to see you again,' and turned her back on us.

The staff grapevine quickly came up with our next digs, one room in the house of a middle-aged, seemingly happy and welcoming couple, Mr and Mrs Dunmore, and we immediately moved in. The room was large, clean, with a double bed, wash basin and open fireplace, on which we did our own cooking, which meant we retained our ration books. It was not long before we realised that Mr and Mrs Dunmore did not enjoy a harmonious marriage. The verbal assaults between them, interspersed with cries of pain, started every night around ten o'clock, and continued until midnight, by when exhaustion had presumably set in and quietness descended. The following mornings we were always greeted with effusive goodwill and smiles.

'Are you happy with your room?' and 'Is there anything you need?' or 'Did you sleep well?'

Obviously they cared for us if not for themselves, but all was not right with our world either.

We were not happy in our jobs, and did not get on with the manager, who appeared to distrust us. Word had reached him from the staff that we were doing our own cooking, and one morning he confronted us.

'A packet of tea is missing from the counter.' His eyes narrowed as he focused on each of us in turn, expecting a confession.

It was nine o'clock and the store had not yet opened. Tea was rationed, and each night the assistant checked that the display was filled, with no gaps.

'We know nothing about it,' we declared, showing our surprise at his insinuation.

His withering look confirmed he did not believe us. That decided us. There were only two leading national retailers on the high street with career structures; Woolworths and Marks and Spencers. We got interviews with M&S, but they assured us that our futures were best with Woolworths, as M&S had fewer than half the number of stores than Woolworths, and promotion was slower. Why should we want to leave Woolworths they asked? We were not convinced and decided to look elsewhere.

Harold came up with an idea.

'Travel,' he said. 'Holidays! People are beginning to look abroad and want to use their currency allowance.'

'They can't go far on that,' I responded.

'France is possible, and Spain,' replied Harold.

He had been to Paris with his mother and could speak a

little of the language. His gestures and charm would make up any deficiencies.

It was 1952, and although the war had been over for seven years, foreign currency exchange was limited to £25 per person per year. The only people I knew who had been abroad had been on His Majesty's service.

'What, you mean apply to Thomas Cook for a job?' I asked.

'No. Go into business ourselves. You could do the administration at this end and I could escort a group to Paris and show them round. We only need to pre-book hotels and the trains.'

'And get the bank credit,' I retorted. 'We've no money, or security!'

'Well, Bert has,' said Harold.

Bert was a fellow trainee manager who had recently come into a small inheritance from his grandfather. He would put money up front for the advertising, brochures, office rental, etc., and we would repay him over time. With little persuasion he agreed to join us.

We decided to start advertising in the spring of the following year, and use the intermediate period to set up business. In the meantime we needed to continue working without our duplicity coming to the attention of an already suspicious store manager. Setting up a business dependent on advertising whilst keeping it under wraps may seem a guarantee of failure, but we did not plan to begin the advertising campaign until the spring and we had the winter to live through.

That Christmas and the New Year were the best I ever had at work. The store staff were not only wonderful workers but knew how to live it up outside of work. We always met many of the girls at dance halls and in the bars. One store supervisor, Milly, married to a baker at Carr's biscuit factory, gave us the key to her house to use if we wished to sleep over. Some of the girls were married to soldiers stationed at the castle and got us entry to the parties that seemed to be held there every night. The New Year was celebrated in the way only Scots can, and although Carlisle may be south of the border, there was many a Scottish kilt flying as we joined in the 'Gay Gordons'.

Nightly rows between Mr and Mrs Dunmore continued during the festive season, but stopped when we eventually complained. Then they no longer spoke to each other in the mornings. Our evenings were busy with preparations, designing and getting brochures printed, doing advertising copy, contacting hotels in Paris, setting the itinerary, and establishing agents. We rented an office in town, registered the name, Ainsworth & Hucknall Tours, and thought we were in business.

'Personally Conducted Tours of Paris. London-return-London. 8 Luxurious Days in residence at Hôtel Imperator & Hôtel du Lion d'Argent. £25 all inclusive. £18 excluding lunch and dinner. Our aim is your satisfaction.'

Setting up the business was the easy part. The hard part was finding the clients. Our advertising launch in March, somewhat limited by our depleted budget, was restricted to two national papers, two inch double columns. We sat back and waited for the response. Over three hundred readers requested our brochures. We repeated the advertisements, and got almost another hundred requests. Our evenings were now taken up with sending brochures and booking forms and addressing envelopes. Then the wait. We did not get the expected avalanche. Booking forms started trickling in and after a month we had only sixty five with deposits, most with different departure dates. We had prescribed a twelve week season, and needed a minimum of twenty people per tour to be in profit. There were not twenty people who wanted to travel on the same date, not even ten. Without funds to continue to advertise we had no option but to return the deposits, to pull down the blind on the stillborn business and renew our commitment to Woolworths, relieved that our business venture had not come to the attention of the manager.

Harold eventually married and prospered as a hotel owner and a gentleman of the Shires, charming the ladies and riding to hounds. Bert bid farewell to his inheritance money and to England, and emigrated to Canada. I continued my career with Woolworths and remained for some months in the bedsit, each evening burning some of the brochures and booking forms in the open fire grate, with a feeling of remorse. Evidence destroyed. Mr and Mrs Dunmore went to Gretna Green to renew their marriage vows and invited me to celebrate their reunion with them when they returned arm-in-arm.

— TWENTY-FIVE —

MORE DIGS

Woolworths did not allow its trainee managers to stagnate in one store for too long. A year or two was the usual time before a move to another store beckoned, and the search for fresh digs resumed. Sometimes one moved into the digs vacated by one's predecessor, but this could have its drawbacks, as it did when I moved from Carlisle to Hull. My predecessor in Hull had left the store with a Don Juan reputation, and indeed had contested a paternity case brought against him by one of the staff. Nonetheless, his sexual proclivities seemed to have left some of the girls adoring his memory, which I could never hope to emulate. Whether he asked to be moved or management in their wisdom moved him was open to question, but as he had no intention of marrying the young mother, the move away was rather propitious for him.

When I knocked on the door at his vacated digs I was greeted most warmly by his ex-landlady, Mrs Harriot, a woman in her mid-fifties, of ample figure, red hair, heavily rouged face, mascara'd eyes and scarlet lips. A *femme fatale* on the doorstep! My startled look got me off on the wrong foot immediately, when at my mention of my predecessor, Billy, she began extolling his virtues.

'Billy was a man about the house,' she said to me with a knowing look, which was lost on me at the time.

'He was so happy here, fitted in so well. Such a pity he had to go.'

Thereafter, for the short time I stayed there, she never stopped telling me how wonderful Billy had been. How he had entertained her with his stories and his mimicry. How he used to make up the fire before leaving for work, gave her a hand with the washing up, fixed the jammed window, and sometimes treated her to a box of Black Magic chocolates. He had obviously spread stardust here as well as at the store. I knew I would never fill Billy's shoes but had no desire to do so. I soon suspected that Billy had not just had his feet under the table but in her bed as well. Whether Mrs Harriot was a widow or a divorcee, or had children, I never knew. She only spoke of the past to me if Billy was mentioned, when her eyes would sparkle at his recollection, and then she would fall silent and look at me dispassionately, knowing that I had put a distance between us.

I was not the only boarder there. The front room was occupied by two actors from the repertory company then playing at the Hull theatre. Peter, the youngest, in his mid-twenties, fair, fresh faced, of slight build and of nervous disposition. He fawned on the older man, Charles, who was pretentious, overweening, and put on a grand air. Always on stage, I thought. Mrs Harriot could not have been more attentive to Charles's wishes than if he had been the King, which, judging by his grand manner, he saw as his role. Mrs Harriot got special food in for him, served it to him in his room, and danced attendance in every way.

Her neighbour, Mrs Massey, was her confidante. She was a friendly, homely woman in her sixties who exuded contentedness. She had an allotment left to her by her late husband, where she kept six laying hens and a cock, which had names, and to which she was devoted. She said they reminded her of her husband, and added, 'although they are more productive than he was'.

Every Monday evening she would arrive at Mrs Harriot's with half a dozen eggs, before they both left for the theatre, when in a usually half-filled auditorium, Charles, Peter and the rest of the cast, gave their first tentative performance of the week's play. Mrs Harriot was given two complimentary tickets each week by Charles, always front stalls, where they led the clapping with enthusiasm, justified or not. It appeared that the eggs were Mrs Massey's payment in kind to Charles, and unsurprisingly, only he was served them. On the weekly occasion I was given an egg, the week's ration, I noticed that it had the Egg Marketing Board symbol on it, a lion, so obviously not an egg from one of Mrs Massey's hens.

I was entertained one Sunday morning when Mrs Harriot asked me to light a fire in their room, as Peter had already tried unsuccessfully, and Charles would never be asked. Thinking that perhaps Billy had been called to do this in the past and that it was an unspoken condition of tenancy, I started to rearrange the kindling, conscious of activity going on behind me. Looking around, I saw that Peter had brought in a galvanised bath, which he and Mrs Harriot started to half fill with hot water carried from the boiler in the scullery. While I was lighting the fire, Charles rose out of his bed, removed his pyjamas and got into the bath. He was indifferent to my presence in the room, or of Mrs Harriot's, who stood on hand ready to administer to his whims. Peter then proceeded to wash Charles, who was sitting in the bath like an overgrown baby.

'Please, please, more hot water,' demanded Charles.

Mrs Harriot scurried out and brought back a bowl of water, tipping it into the bath.

'Aah, enough, enough, aah, aah aah,' sighed Charles.

Peter tittered and, rather lingeringly, washed Charles's back with a flannel.

As the fire took hold, Charles obliquely acknowledged my presence for the first time.

'Ah, wonderful. A fire, the gift of the gods!'

Bloody cheek, I thought.

Charles rose from the bath and Peter began to towel him down.

'Thank you, darling,' said Charles, taking the towel and

wrapping it around himself.

As I left the room, Peter started to undress, ready to take Charles' place in the bath. Same water, I thought, wondering if Charles would dry *him* down, but somehow doubting it.

Mrs Harriot was by my side in the lobby.

'He has a wonderful body, hasn't he?'

'Who?' I asked.

'Why, Charles of course. He can hold the audience in raptures.'

'Is this performance usual?' I asked cynically.

'Every day,' she said, 'It's all very natural to Charles. Wonderful man!'

It was soon apparent to me that I was one too many for this *ménage à trois*, in fact and in inclination. Mrs Harriot's preoccupation with Charles's demands left her little time to keep the house clean and, as the food was barely palatable, I started to look for alternative accommodation. I gave Mrs Harriot the customary week's notice.

'I knew you weren't like Billy when you came,' was her response. 'He was very happy here, but if you don't like it, I hope you get something to suit you. Theatricals are better anyway,' she added, turning her back on me.

A cashier at the bank had told me he was moving on, and would be vacating his digs. He introduced me to his landlady, Mrs Deacon, a widow in her forties, with a schoolgirl daughter. She had an amiable manner, and I immediately felt comfortable moving into her semi-detached house. Mrs Deacon confided in me that she was thinking of having another boarder to further supplement her income, and if I had no objection, it would be a young woman who had been referred to her by the hospital.

'Her name is Kate. She has been treated in hospital following a nervous breakdown, but she is alright now and works in an office in town.'

Kate moved in and a rapport between everyone was soon

established. Mrs Deacon was an easy person to get along with and Kate appeared to be a quiet and reserved woman in her early thirties. We caught the same bus to work together and established an easy familiarity. She had been with us for three weeks when one night I was awakened in my sleep and, on opening my eyes, saw Kate in my bedroom standing in front of the dressing table stark naked.

'Kate, what are you doing?'

Kate had her eyes open but made no answer, went to the window and looked out. I thought I had better waken Mrs Deacon before unpredictable consequences followed.

'What on earth are you doing, Katy?' repeated Mrs Deacon as she came in.

Again there was no response.

'Come, I think you should be in your own room,' said Mrs Deacon, leading her out. 'Lay down in your bed and go to sleep.'

Mrs Deacon came back to my room.

'She doesn't seem conscious. I think she must be sleepwalking.'

I had to agree. There was no other explanation. Next morning when we questioned Kate and related the events to her, she had no recollection of them.

Some days later when I returned from work in the evening, Mrs Deacon met me with an extraordinary story.

An elderly German couple was staying with their daughter two houses away. All the houses in the street were identical, semi-detached. The visiting German couple did not know any of the neighbours, knew no English, and their daughter was at work. The woman was resting in bed and her husband was having a bath, when the bathroom door opened and in came Kate who immediately started undressing. The surprised German, lost for English words, quickly got out of the bath, and Kate got in. The man woke his wife, who remonstrated with Kate in German, but to no avail. They went next door for help, but not being understood, beckoned the hesitant neighbour into their house and bathroom. The neighbour had no idea what to expect, but it was not a nude woman.

'Why, she is from Mrs Deacon's, number fifteen!' The neighbour told the uncomprehending German couple. 'I'll go and get Mrs Deacon.'

Fortunately Mrs Deacon was at home and came at once, induced Kate out of the bath, dried and dressed her, and took her back home. Kate offered no reason or apology and seemed unaware of anything amiss. Mrs Deacon was having none of it. She telephoned the hospital which had made the referral and duly an ambulance arrived to take Kate back. Poor Kate. She may simply have mistaken the house number, or had a tendency to sleepwalk even in daytime. Mrs Deacon hesitated about getting another boarder. Her daughter said she did not want another woman in the house anyway and, if her mother was to have anybody, to make sure it was a man – a view which I unhesitatingly endorsed. Unfortunately, it never came to pass.

— TWENTY-SIX —

GOOD LORD DELIVER US*

Hull city in the 1950s was a prosperous fishing and commercial port employing thousands in mainly manual work and, because of this, and its relative isolation on the Humber river, its inhabitants had developed a hardy, independent character. Having also been the most heavily bombed city outside of London in the Second World War, with over half the population made homeless, they had literally been tested through fire.

Being near the docks, the Woolworths store was infested by rats, and one of the last jobs at night before leaving was to place rat traps behind the counters. These were pieces of cardboard layered with strong thick glue and some morsel of food. Next morning, the first job was to collect the catch, knock out any rats still alive and dispose of them. Many rats escaped by gnawing through a leg or foot and leaving it on the board. It was not uncommon for rats to be seen when the store was open, and on one occasion when I saw one running around the cornice, I hit it on the head with a broom. Its tail got caught and the stunned rat was left swinging in public view until I got it into a sack and drowned it in an ever-ready bucket of water.

Although the rats didn't seem to deter custom, we attracted more customers by holding two big sale events each year, and made sure the whole city knew of them, using posters, leaflets and a brass band. With supermarkets not yet having crossed over from America, Woolworths were the main retailers along with Marks and Spencer and never considered it necessary to advertise nationally. A queue of shoppers would form at sale time before the store opened to snap up the bargains and the many items which were still in short supply. We released balloons advertising the sale from the roof of the store, attracting crowds which had to be dispersed by the police. I hired a horse and dressed in cowboy gear and with a placard on my back, rode it around the city, even attempting, unsuccessfully, to ride into M&S.

The Woolworths store manager was a Glaswegian called Jack Dawson, who, appropriately for Hull, was a fish in water, except that water rarely passed his lips. He was a mild-mannered and capable manager in the mornings when he was sober. At midday he would take the previous day's takings to the bank after which he would make for his reserved stool by the bar in the old and much-celebrated 'White Hart' pub, in the street called the Land of Green Ginger, not far from the store. He was a consummate Scotch whisky drinker, and could down a bottle before returning to the store in late afternoon, a changed man, with his Glaswegian accent more difficult to understand, his stance uncertain, his eye for fault more acute, and his manner more intimidating. The largely female staff then avoided him if they could, some taking to hiding under the counter if they saw him approaching. Even customers who knew him avoided him. He quickly recognised what he considered to be undesirables in the store. They may have been shoplifters or drunks, both of whom seemed to proliferate, but more likely they were long-haired youths or newly emergent Teddy boys.

He would approach one of the assistant managers and, with a nod of the head, indicate some unsuspecting individual, who had caught his attention.

'See him out,' he would order.

It may have been an innocent dockworker or fisherman who was more sober than himself, but he would not give ground until the man was shown out of the store. This led to many unwarranted confrontations. Not surprisingly there were often fights in the store which spilled out onto the pavement. Having instigated the incident he never followed it up physically himself, his excuse being that an injured arm disabled him from doing so. He left the problem he created for others to resolve.

Like many alcoholics he tried to hide his intake. His wife was also from Glasgow and was a gin addict. They met in the Station Hotel, usually at weekends when they invited me to join them. I agreed only if I could not think of an excuse for not doing so. After ordering drinks in the upstairs bar in the pillared lounge, Jack would then leave his wife on the pretence of going to the downstairs toilet where there was another bar but instead, to have another whisky, knock it back, and order a refill to be ready on the bar for his next 'toilet visit'. This deception he played on his wife gave him immense satisfaction and would go on all evening.

When closing time came, getting a taxi driver to take them home was always a problem. Jack was a notoriously poor payer and ran up bills with anyone and everyone. His request to 'get him a taxi' usually meant having to pay the driver before he was allowed into it.

Jack's habitual drinking sometimes gave him hallucinations. Fire buckets filled with water or sand, were kept behind every counter, with the water changed every week by the assistants. On several occasions he accused staff of stealing money by putting silver coins into a water bucket before going out to change the water.

'Look,' he said, pointing to the bucket, 'Half-crowns.'

There were no half-crowns, but he could not be convinced. Occasionally the innocent assistant broke down in tears and had to be consoled, but in one instance, a bucket of water was thrown over him by one accused assistant. Yet, when sober he could show concern for his staff, sending flowers if they had a bereavement or wedding, and being considerate in many ways. Despite his drunken behaviour the Hull staff had amazing loyalty towards him. Jack lived until retiring at sixty, but to no one's surprise, died shortly afterwards of cirrhosis of the liver.

My next assignment was to the delightful Victorian seaside town of Scarborough. I had upped my standards in accommodation and, going with the trend, gave up on digs and instead rented a bedsit with a Mr and Mrs Brown. They were dependable and considerate, even cleaning my room and providing breakfast. Enlivening the house were four members of a girls band, except that by no stretch of the imagination could they qualify as 'girls', all of them being over forty. They were playing Scarborough for the season. The band leader had been an instrumentalist for the formidable Ivy Benson, and her 'All Girls Band', before forming her own all female band. The violinist Max Jaffa was the perennial attraction at the Spa, often broadcasting from there. The Laughtons were running the Pavilion Hotel, and their son, Charles, and his wife, Elsa Lanchester, were occasional visitors. They revelled in their fame and were gregarious after a few drinks in the bar. His brother Tom had a coterie of gay friends, whom I sometimes drank with at weekends, but they were all pretentious and backbiting and I felt out of place.

Besides, I had other things I wanted to do. At weekends, I often went to the cinema. It was 1956, the year of the Suez *débacle* and the release of the first rock-and-roll film *Rock Around The Clock*. The film was banned in some towns for inciting rowdy behaviour, but was shown in Scarborough where I joined the long queue of teenagers to see it. It was a boisterous audience with attendants trying to keep would-be dancers in their seats. Suez and rock were two unconnected events but both heralded change in the country and its influence in the world.

A driving school in the town was offering a course of five driving lessons at a reduced rate of £5 and, always with my eye on a bargain, I enrolled for the course. Although I made fitful progress, I nevertheless put in for my test. When the day came, I drove off with the examiner beside me, but felt that the engine was not pulling as it should. I pressed harder on the accelerator.

'The car would go better without the handbrake on,' said the examiner caustically.

Failed already, I thought, as I released the handbrake. With nervous apprehension I finished the test and waited for the expected thumbs down.

'I'm passing you, allowing for your nervousness. You took no notice of the man on the corner giving traffic signals. He was not authorised to do so, so you were right to ignore him.'

Fortunately I had not even noticed the man.

'You're the only person I've passed today,' he said, by way of an explanation.

It was the end of the day, and his tone suggested that he had to justify his job by passing someone. I was fortunate as, because of the Suez crisis and the consequent petrol rationing, there was little traffic on the roads. It would be three years before I bought a car and drove again.

The store manager was Reg Wilson, who preferred to be addressed as Major Wilson, although eight years had elapsed since he had held that position in the army. He was a snob. Aloof, unapproachable, contemptuous, he could maintain silence for several days if offended or confronted. His *hauteur* set him apart from his staff who consequently had little loyalty towards him. His superiority was put to the test when he requested a supplier to falsify an invoice, a transaction he would have benefitted from. One of the rules in the Company rule book was that no direct contact could be made to a supplier. The supplier reported the request to head office in London, where he was instructed to report for interview. I was told to accompany him. His job, and his pension, were on the line, as he admitted to me on our train journey to London. The only way out was denial, and he begged me to endorse his lie. We were interviewed separately and we each denied the accusation. It was our word against the supplier. It was not a court of law, so perjury was not committed, but I felt very guilty, although my guilt was sweetened by seeing the man humiliated and his ego remained deflated for some time afterwards.

It was with relief that my next move was to Halifax, but the relief was short lived. The manager, one Leonard Scott, ran his store as his personal fiefdom.

On my first morning he called a staff meeting and introduced me, saying if I was any good, my previous manager would have not let me go. I soon learnt that, like all bullies, you only have their respect when you stand up to them, and the opportunity soon came when he caught me in the stockroom, when according to his self-imposed rule, I should have been on the sales floor. He crept up behind me and surprised me with a blow on the back of my head and I immediately retaliated with my fist in his chest. The punch took the wind out of him and he did not return it, but I had begun to gain his respect. He was in his fifties; a stout, country-looking, red-faced man with piercing brown eyes and a challenging and authoritative manner. Trade union membership was not Company policy, so the staff had no one to represent their interests. Few staff stayed long, and he preferred to employ part-timers as they had fewer privileges and holidays. Woolworths store managers had an almost autocratic control of their stores, and within certain parameters imposed from head office, imposed their own style and standards.

Leonard Scott's management was unlike any other. He insisted on staff being on the sales floor thirty minutes before opening time, when he would orchestrate them into a choir to sing rousing songs. After closing the store in the evenings, he would challenge other male staff to put on boxing gloves to spar with him. In winter, before opening, he would lead the staff on an indoor run to warm up, snaking through the counters, offices and stockrooms, to compensate for the lack of heating in the store. Although married and with a family, he was in an extramarital relationship with Amy, the office manager, an attractive, lively woman in her forties. On his retirement, they bought a camper van, and were known to enjoy a blissful carefree lifestyle together travelling around Europe. Fortunately I did not have to endure his autocratic management style that long as, after a year, I was on the next step of the ladder.

* 'From Hull, from Halifax, from Hell, tis thus, from all these three, Good Lord deliver us.' 'Beggar's Litany' by John Taylor (1580–1654)

— Twenty-Seven —

A RUNG ON THE LADDER

The director looked at me across the expanse of his oak desk, silently weighing me up me before deliberately intoning his words with authority.

'We have decided to appoint you to store management'.

I feigned a look of surprise and what I hoped was appreciation of his munificence. It would not go down well if I showed that I had been expecting a promotion. What had I been working towards for these last seven years if it was not this?

Continuing to endeavour to impress me with his efficiency and that words were money and not to be wasted, he brushed aside my attempted 'thank you'.

'Your first store is Morley in West Yorkshire. What profit you make is up to you, but that is what you will be paid on. My secretary will give you all the information you need. Report there on Monday when the superintendent will be there to make the handover. Congratulations!'

At last I was rid of working under oppressive managers and now had my own store, although a small one, and with five bigger classes of stores I was on the bottom rung of the ladder.

The director rose to shake hands.

'One word of caution; don't take advantage of the staff.'

Twenty female staff were safe from sexual advances from me, but he was not to know and I was not about to enlighten him. I was well used to everyone assuming that I was sexually attracted to women, and, like most other unacknowledged homosexuals, went along with the pretence. The alternative was to be ostracised, discriminated against, assaulted, blackmailed, ridiculed or face possible police harassment. It was 1957 and homosexuality was not only little talked about but was still illegal.

It was without regret that I put Halifax behind me and made the short journey by bus from Halifax to Morley. I had no car, no partner, no bank balance, and no accommodation, but that was soon rectified when, on my second day, an elderly woman stopped me.

'Are you the new manager? I hear you're looking for accommodation.'

I was well aware that Yorkshire folk were open and friendly which could often be construed as prying, so the implied offer did not surprise me. Word had apparently got round that Woolworths had a new manager and I was being acknowledged by some shoppers.

I readily accepted the roof over my head which Mrs Holdsworth offered and she and her husband welcomed me as one of the family. They were a true Yorkshire couple, direct and down to earth, never giving 'out for nowt', and determined to deflate unwarranted egos.

'Never 'ave time for folks with airs and graces,' she said, 'And you don't seem to have any.'

I took that as a compliment, thinking it went with the other things I did not have. Having so few possessions put me on favourable terms, as long as I 'did not get above myself', a sin which, to them, should have been the eleventh commandment. Knowing only too well my own shortcomings, there was little chance of that, and I was happy to accept their hospitality on their terms.

The 'family' was their only son, his wife and their two boys, who lived nearby. The son had land in the 'Rhubarb Triangle', an area located between Morley, Wakefield and Rothwell and grew rhubarb commercially. Fortunately I liked rhubarb and had it in all its variations: with custard, in pies, rhubarb fool, crumble, jams and trifles. All part of the 'plain

Yorkshire food' which Mrs Holdsworth prided herself in cooking and serving in enormous helpings, and any food left on the plate she viewed as a reproach of her cooking skills.

Morley was then a prosperous market town, famous for its town hall and its production of 'Shoddy', a cloth made from the recovery of wool from rags, and the waste product used to fertilise the rhubarb fields. The acrid oily smell of the production process permeated the town and the millworkers too. Like Rome, but in no other respects, it was built on seven hills. There was still much of the northern industrial nineteenth century character to be seen; rows of back-to-back houses, cobbled streets, chapels for the nonconformists, thriving woollen mills, and smoking chimneys. The inhabitants seemed proud of their town, sure of its permanence in their life, and, if born there, with little wish to live anywhere else.

The staff of twenty women and Fred the stockroom boy were willing workers, who let me know that they needed little management from me. Unlike my predecessor, who was happy to take a siesta each afternoon and leave the staff to get on with their jobs, I was keen to exert my new management role. Fortunately I had the support of the most senior staff member, the cashier, Miss Oakroyd, who had been looking in vain for romance in her life, and saw a glimmer of it in me.

With the larger stores of Leeds and Bradford on its fringes taking the big money, Morley was dependent on the everyday shopping, and Woolworths was still the 'Nothing over Sixpence' store in people's minds. We had a sale event coming up and I needed to get additional customers into the store spending more; and also there was an inter-store competition for the biggest sales increase. On my talk to the staff, I asked them, did they want to participate? They rose to the challenge, soliciting orders from friends and family, and delivering leaflets in the town. I hired loudspeakers and played music interspersed with sale announcements, hoping it would stir the shoppers into parting with their 'brass'. It certainly stirred up the other traders, who joined together to protest until I turned the volume down.

On the day of the sale, a queue formed outside before opening time, something never seen since the days of rationing. Our efforts proved a success and we won the competition and prize money of £5 each employee, to be spent in celebration.

'How are we going to celebrate?' the staff wanted to know.

A party? A night out to a Leeds theatre? A trip to Blackpool?

'What about a trip to London?' asked Miss Oakroyd. 'I've never been there.'

'Neither have I!' came the chorus, then, 'What shall we do when we get there?'

'See a show of course!'

Shops closed one half-day a week then, but that day the store closed all day and the staff, leaving their children, husbands, and responsibilities behind, and with one mind, set out in an old pre-war charabanc to enjoy themselves. London was two hundred miles away but all the more time to sing songs, raise laughs, and talk. Not only to tour the sights of London, but also to see Van Johnson, starring in the musical 'The Music Man'.

Travelling back at night gave everyone time to reflect.

'No, London was alright, but I wouldn't want to live there. Too crowded, too expensive and the people were not friendly. Give us Morley any day!' was the consensus, a view not shared by me; give me London, but I kept the thought to myself.

'Nearly home now. Goodnight Masie! Goodnight Sue! Goodnight Mr Hucknall! See you tomorrow, at work, if you're lucky!'

It had not been my first visit to London and, although all

the visits had been brief, I knew that was where I really wanted to be. For now, the nearby city of Leeds would have to provide compensation, while Miss Oakroyd's tentative advances received no nourishment and withered on the vine.

For the first time in my life I was not amongst other males whose sexual mores I felt I had to conform to. Whether in school, the army, in college, or as a trainee manager, if I was to be accepted by my male collegues, I knew I had to hide my sexuality. Now, without such close comparisons, I felt some release from these self-imposed restraints, but opportunities for gay contact were few and fortuitous.

For most gay men sexual encounters were limited to a few questionable bars or in public toilets, but any loitering could lead to an arrest. It was not unknown for zealous plain-clothed officers to entice men's interest and then arrest the victim for importuning. On a necessary visit to one toilet, a man standing next to me gave me a weak smile. I half smiled back. He appeared respectable, and was my own age. This could be interesting, I thought. He looked down and I felt the tension of the moment. I too looked down, but it was his shoes I noticed. Black, thick soled, suggested police issue to me, and I felt nervous. I zipped up and left, only to be followed by him. I thought that I would lead him a dance, and made for the next toilet, half a mile away, conscious of him following me, but I did not go in, and instead quickly hopped on to a passing bus. He was one policeman who was not getting an easy conviction.

I occasionally visited the bar at Leeds City Hotel and arriving one evening rather early, I found only one other person there. He turned his head towards me and gave me a welcoming smile as if he knew me.

'Hello. My name is Wilfred. What will you have?'

It was not customary to be offered a drink by a stranger. He was a cheerful-looking, well-mannered, middle-aged man, impeccably dressed in a suit with a pink shirt and a gold

Rolex on his wrist.

'Thank you, but I will get my own,' I said, trying not to sound too discourteous.

'Quiet tonight, isn't it?'

He must be all of forty-five, I thought.

'Yes, not much happens at any time here.'

'Well, I'm staying here!' he said, raising a laugh.

We continued chatting, making conversation about Leeds and the state of the country, before he offered me another drink.

'Or we could go up to my room and have it in more comfort. What do you think?'

No, I thought, older men don't attract me.

'No, thank you, I must be going soon.'

'What a pity. I'm sure we could find so much in common.'

He was not offended by my refusal but continued being pleasant with wry humour and flattery. I felt the pressure to accede to his entreaties rising and rather than succumb to them, I thanked him for his invitation, bade him farewell and departed.

It was five years later, when, turning on the television to watch a new comedy series, 'Steptoe and Son', I recognised his face behind the grimacing and sneering. He was Steptoe and, in his mastery of the role, so different to the agreeable, elegant man I had refused a one night stand with.

— TWENTY-EIGHT —

A RUN DOWN THE M1

My next step up the ladder occurred two years later when I was given the management of the Woolworth store in Wellingborough, Northamptonshire. It was 1959, when the first section of the new motorway, the M1, reached Northamptonshire from London, heralding a new dawn for motoring.

It was also the year I bought my first car, a second-hand, racing green, MG Roadster. I was thirty and, although I had passed my driving test three years before, I had never driven since. The previous owner brought the car and parked it outside the front door in my street, a cul-de-sac, where I left it until the following Sunday morning thinking it would be a quiet day to try out my driving skills.

I rose early, before any neighbours would be up and about, put the key into the ignition, turned on the motor and, recalling the earlier mishap on my driving test, released the handbrake and gently pressed the accelerator. Much to my surprise, the car moved forward. I was driving, slowly and hesitatingly and proceeding with caution when a milk float turned into the narrow cul-de-sac. An experienced driver would have passed it by without difficulty. Not being an experienced driver, I managed to get my front bumper locked into a wheel of the milk float and neither I nor the milkman could extricate it. By now the neighbours were aroused and two of them came out obligingly to lend a hand, much to my embarrassment. With the four of us taking a wheel each, we lifted the car out of its engagement with the milk float and, with more neighbours emerging from their homes to watch the proceedings, the only damage was to my self esteem. So began my motoring experience.

With the opening of the motorway, and no speed limit yet imposed, the joy of driving on it was exhilarating. This was going to be the future. I could drive to London in under an hour and park for free in the West End with no traffic wardens or parking meters. My world was opening up. Now London's nightlife was available to me. Theatre visits, chats and chaps in discreet bars, then a visit to a Turkish bath, could all be done in one night.

In one of the best Turkish baths, in Jermyn Street, it was possible to stay all night. After undressing and nonchalantly wrapping towels around their waists, clients would saunter about, surveying the reclining bodies and assessing the prospects the night held, before a visit to the hot rooms where serious sweating was silently maintained for as long as one could stand the heat. Next was the relaxation of the cooling room, or, if preferred, a vigorous massage, before being wrapped in dry towels by an attendant who would then show one to an available bed; the occupants of other beds seeming to be asleep, or maintaining the pretence of sleeping, but more likely laying awake ready to catch the eye of any new arrival with the physical attributes to arouse their passion. Cubicles were also available where a night's sleep would not be violated or where intimacies could be enjoyed without the prying eyes of others, although voyeurs would always be prowling around under the dimmed lights anxious to gratify their sexual curiosity. I knew of no hotel which could offer better room service.

There was no gay life in Wellingborough that I was aware of, and very little of any other sort of life. It was a conservative market town, prosperous and satisfied with itself. The first Caribbean family arrived in 1959 and was conspicuous by their uniqueness. Tesco opened its most northern store opposite me the same year, giving the Company its first real competition, but Woolworths was celebrating its Golden Jubilee, 50 years of trading in the UK. It moved its UK head office from Bond Street, in London, to a new purpose-built office in Marylebone Street. All staff were asked to contribute a token one penny each towards its construction and all the thousands of employees readily responded. It now had over one thousand branches and was the second largest company on the London Stock Exchange.

The Company's first ever television advertising was launched, breaking previous embargos on national advertising. Every employee was treated to a dinner, dance and party at a local hotel. Store managers, however, joined top brass in something more grandiose; a convention at the ultramodern Royal Festival Hall, followed by a banquet at London's Dorchester Hotel; very much a celebratory, backslapping endorsement of the Company.

After the banquet a group of fellow managers, some of whom I knew, approached me.

'We're going to the Stork Club in Piccadilly. Are you joining us?'

With their egos inflated, and testosterone rising, they were obviously ready to be seduced by London's nightlife. No thank you, I wanted to say. Why not tell them that I was not interested in philandering with women? That my own predilection was towards men? How would they react if they knew? Was I prepared to be ostracised by them?

'OK I'll join you,' I said, with some reluctance, a feeling of boredom already settling on me.

On the way, a manager I did not know, walked alongside me.

'You didn't sound very enthusiastic, friend,' he said, with a smile.

'No, I'm not. Sorry if it showed, anyway I didn't feel like going straight back to the hotel.'

More subterfuge, I thought. Why cannot I be honest with people, instead of covering up my real feelings?

'It might have been better to go back,' he said, 'One never knows.'

Was he just being friendly, I asked myself, or was he really insinuating something?

On arrival at the club, we were welcomed by a burly doorman and greeted inside by a line-up of eager 'hostesses', or, as I saw them, praying mantises. Each hostess quickly picked her target. I saw one looming towards me.

'Good evening, darling. How are you? How lovely to see you here. Do make yourself comfortable, and tell me about yourself.'

She feigned a smile as she heaved her bust towards me, her blonde hair – or was it a wig? – falling over her bare shoulders.

A waiter brought a champagne looking bottle to our table.

'Can I serve the lady, sir?'

She put her hand on my thigh.

'I would very much like it,' she said ambiguously.

What was I doing here? Did she take me for the provincial punter she was setting me up as? Looking around, I saw fellow managers looking as though heaven had fallen into their laps as they each responded to the intimations of their hostesses. Not waiting for an answer from me, the waiter opened the bottle and filled two glasses, leaving the bottle on the table. My hostess lifted her glass to her lips and half emptied it.

'I'm Sue. What's your name?'

Her smile hardened as she realised that I was not the easy catch she was hoping for.

'Joe,' I said, trying to sound as disinterested as I felt, without being surly.

'What do you do, Joe?'

She refilled her glass.

'As little as possible.'

'You're not drinking,' she said, pouting her lips.

Her beguiling look failed to entice me.

'Will you excuse me? I must go to the toilet,' I said as I got up.

On my way, I met some of my group whose libido was evidently on the wane and who were discussing whether to leave. I said we were being taken for suckers and it was best to get out. Some said that they had taken a drink and therefore felt obliged to pay, whilst others said they had neither ordered nor drunk anything. We made towards the exit, and were confronted by two dinner-suited bouncers, who said that we had a bill to settle first. My friends started arguing with them, while I turned back towards the toilet. The manager who had come with me left the group, followed me to the toilet, and stood beside me.

'This is a right clip joint,' he said. 'Not my scene at all.'

'Nor mine either.'

I felt an empathy between us. Could he be thinking what I was thinking?

'Which hotel are you staying in?' he asked.

'The Regent Palace.'

'Ah, same as me. I'm in room 440 on the fourth floor,' he said diffidently.

My perception was right. Our thoughts were on the same wavelength.

'Oh, I'm on the third, room 336,' I said. 'You're welcome to call in for a drink.'

'James the name,' he said, holding out his hand.

'Joe,' I responded, taking his hand. He pressed a finger deliberately into my palm. I was now sure we were two of a kind.

I zipped up.

'First thing is to get out of this place with our wallets intact,' I said.

Back in the club our group was now arguing with the manager of the club.

'He said the bill is £240 for the champagne.'

'There was no champagne. It was just fizz.'

The manager put on a patient look.

'You don't expect to come in here and be entertained and drink for nothing, do you?'

'We're being ripped off. The best thing is to call for the police,' I said.

The manager held up his hands, 'Look, you've come from out of town. I'll make a deduction as you haven't been here long. Call it £180.'

I thought that £30 each was a price worth paying for an experience never to be repeated, and to get out of the place. We all seemed to be in agreement. As we each put our money down, I looked over to my table. Sue was still there, but with another punter. She looked up, smiled, and waved goodbye.

On our way out, James and I lingered at the back of the group, which was splitting up to go to different hotels.

Returning to our hotel, James said, 'I'll take you up on your offer,' and got into the lift with me. What was I doing, I asked myself? Where will this lead? James looked a decent guy, older than me, perhaps forty, but did I want to compromise myself with another Woolworths manager?

As soon as the lift doors closed he pressed himself against me and, rather tentatively, kissed me. We were still kissing when the lift stopped on the third floor, and James followed me to my room. That night, for the first time in my life, I felt relaxed in another man's arms.

He was gone when I awoke next morning, but there was a note under the door. 'Lovely to have met you, but I'm sorry I can't see you again. I'm married. Hope you understand.'

So it was just a one night stand after all. I wanted to meet him to tell him that I did not want to see him again either, but our paths never crossed again. I drew the line at married men. I had enough duplicity in my life already.

— TWENTY-NINE —

A TASTE OF LIBERATION

There was a placidity about Northamptonshire, a feeling of being at ease with itself. It was 'Middle England', 1959, and Harold Macmillan had returned a Conservative government to power. His boast that the nation had 'never had it so good', had been made in the nearby town of Bedford, and affirmed the well-being of both counties, more than it did of the inhabitants of the north. Like a chameleon, I was always ready to adapt to change and I slipped into the relaxed character of the county with the same ease. I made contact with the local stables and resumed horse riding on Sunday mornings, my first outing on horses since my canters on the Southport sands nine years before. Early on Sunday mornings the countryside was quiet and, as I rode through the lanes and soft low hills spread out before me, I felt that I had it all to myself and that *I* had never had it so good.

It was not long before I met Jasper, a jockey who worked in the stables, and we often rode together, usually galloping too quickly for my inexperience. Jasper was a very frustrated gay young man, terrified of his sexual orientation becoming known to his fellow jockeys. His pent-up emotions exploded into passion when unleashed. He confided in me, after one passionate ingress, that he was attracted to sadomasochism, and tentatively suggested that we experiment with it. The thought repelled me and I told him so, after which his interest in me quickly abated and I resumed riding on my own.

Holidays abroad, so long prohibitively expensive to most people, were opening up and in 1959, I booked a holiday to San Sebastian in Spain with my younger brother, Reg, who also was still single. After booking the holiday, Reg told me that he had met and fallen in love with a girl called Maureen, a redhead like himself. For days into the holiday he was morose and silent, and even going to a bull fight failed to arouse him.

'What is the matter?' I asked in exasperation. 'I know it's rained every day we've been here, but don't you think we should make the most of it?'

'I'm missing Maureen and just want to get back to her,' he said despondently.

The rain was relentless as was Reg's lovesickness and we spent most of the holiday drinking brandy in bars with Basque fishermen, before returning to the UK. It was not long after when they announced their engagement and marriage quickly followed. The adage, 'marry in haste, repent at leisure', was never more appropriate, but their union did have one happy outcome. It gave birth to Mick Hucknall, aka 'Simply Red'.

With a holiday 'privilege' now of four weeks a year from work, I was determined to spend these abroad, preferably on my own. It was not just a need for freedom from sexual repression enforced on homosexuals, but also a wish to escape from the familiar and the predictable environment. The country was in one of its ever-recurring economic crises. Macmillan's boast of 'never having it so good' had come back to haunt him and, by 1961, he had imposed a wage freeze because of the country's balance of payment problems. With the economic malaise, I gave serious thought to working abroad, but decided to see more countries first. Morocco and Portugal attracted me. On the surface they appeared to be tolerant societies, cheap places to live in, and expats seemed to be having a good life.

I travelled throughout Morocco in a hired car and was enthralled by its exoticism and laid back lifestyle. The first thing I learnt was to be suspicious of friendliness. Everyone held out a hand in friendship, usually with something to sell in their other hand and sometimes in their heart. The second thing was not to be surprised. Sleeping under the stars one night in the Atlas mountains, I awoke to find a Berber sitting by my side, holding a rifle, his brown leathery face half hidden by a black scarf. He spoke fluent French and claimed to have been protecting me from bandits whilst I slept, but following his tradition of hospitality, refused my proffered payment. Life for these Berber tribesmen and their families must have been as hard as the ground I slept on, but they were as welcoming as they were proud. They lived out their lives in isolated villages of brown, mud built houses, occasionally meeting up with other village communities for festivals or the occasional feria regional. On approaching a village, a group of excited and smiling children would run out in welcome. They became even more excited when thrown a handful of balloons, which I had been advised to carry.

Marrakesh, at the foot of the High Atlas Mountains, attracts Moroccan and overseas visitors alike, all out to abandon themselves to the rhythm of African drums, snake charmers and story tellers, in the 'Meeting Place of the Dead'. I revelled in the freedom from restraint, smoked my first hash, danced and embraced unknown young men and slept with them on roof tops open to the sky. During the day, a young Arab appointed himself as my 'minder' and for a small payment, never left my side. When the heat was insufferable, I spent most of the time in the swimming pool with my head under the water for as long as possible.

The temperature in Tangiers was not as oppressive, but the attention from the street boys and traders was. Within a few minutes, I was offered an incredible variety of things for sale from snake skins to writhing snakes, from sex with boys to fossilized ammonites, as well as meals and drinks in bars, and guides of all ages offering their services of themselves and to the city's numerous attractions, nefarious or not.

One day I met another Englishman, named Arthur, who

said he came to Tangiers every year.

'What a crazy place this is,' he said. 'I'm worn out by all the attention I'm getting.'

'Where do you go?' I asked.

'To saunas. Why not come along with me?'

With the heat outside, I could only think of a sauna as the last place I would want to visit, so I politely declined. I met him the next day in the hotel. He looked frayed and nervous.

'I dare not go out,' he said. 'I know if I do the boys will be waiting for me, and I'm fucked up already. Will you have a drink and stay with me a while?'

We sat down together and he told me he was the landlord of a country pub in Kent, married, with two grown-up sons.

'They would kill me if they knew what I got up to,' he said. 'They hate queers. I'm terrified that if they even suspected, they would kill me.'

Arthur was a kindly man, compassionate and with money available to anyone with a sad story. He was very generous to his young men, or 'boys' as he called them, which made him a target for all the rent boys in Tangiers. Not long after meeting me, he made one visit too many to a sauna and died of a heart attack there. His sons came to Tangiers to escort his body home, asked surprisingly few questions, preferring to remain either unaware of their father's sexual proclivities, or not wishing their suspicions to be confirmed.

Hospitality was natural in the Arab culture, and invitations to visit their homes and families frequently had to be politely refused. After bargaining and buying an Arabic brass plate one day from a man in his workshop, I did accept his invitation. He pulled down the shutter and escorted me to his riad at the back of his workshop. He showed me into a room layered with carpets and cushions on the floor and invited me to lie down. His two young sons were sitting there very quietly and contentedly, before rising to shake my hand. His wife entered and he spoke to her, then with scarcely a glance at me, she left the room. After a few minutes she returned with a pot of mint tea and glasses, and immediately left again. The artisan spoke good English, and told me that his father and his grandfather had been brass workers, and he hoped his sons would be too. No doubt also with docile wives who would accept their imposed inferiority, I thought. Before I left, he insisted I accept another plate from him as a gift.

With foreign travel now more accessible, I flew abroad whenever work allowed. There was an intimacy in flying then with no security hassle. On one flight to Milan on the later defunct airline 'Dan Air', I was invited to sit in the cockpit, alongside the first pilot, who I was surprised to find was a female, the only one, I learnt, then flying commercial planes.

Visits to California, Bali, Hong Kong, Thailand, Greece, all beckoned and did not disappoint. Being single and on a good salary allowed me the freedom. Once abroad, I could cut the constraints of conformity. Very likely they were constraints I put upon myself, but at home, I was very responsive to other people's expectations of me. They had been ingrained into me from childhood, by having an authoritarian father and an awareness of my family's parameters.

The release from constraints sometimes found me in unexpected and precarious situations. With a smile or an inference, casual friendships could be made and sex indulged in surprising places. A dentist's chair in Athens, on a plane from Lisbon, in a cave in the Atlas mountains – anywhere was possible, but such moments of passion were brief and without commitment. I wanted something more, but it was elusive and a criminal offence in my country; a same sex partner to live with and love.

— THIRTY —

RAY'S BAR

Spain was attracting an increasing number of overseas residents and investments, but I was more interested in Portugal. Salazar had been in power since 1932 as prime minister and president, and although he still ran an authoritarian regime, with secret police, the signs were that it was coming to an end and the country was opening up.

I decided to explore the possibilities of an *émigré* lifestyle and booked into the Grand Hotel, at Monte Estoril. In the evening I strolled into a bar opposite, signed up as 'Ray's – Cocktail Lounge and Bar'. Inside it was dimly lit, with walls layered with strips of fine cork, only illuminated by lights above several oil portraits and spotlights on antique classical figures. One painting which stood out was of a young man, stripped to the waist, laying a stone path. There were comfortable cane chairs around the room but I took a seat at the marble-topped bar, on one of the high red leather topped stools. I was the only customer.

'Good evening, sir'.

The greeting came from the man behind the bar who was polishing glasses. I noticed his eyes first, brown, warm, alert, welcoming with an implicit look of approval. He was of slight build, with a tanned skin, and neatly dressed. I ordered a glass of wine.

'Ah, English, I think,' he said, by way of opening conversation. 'London?'

'No, we don't all come from London,' I responded, somewhat unkindly. 'Actually, I'm from the north of England. And you, you are American, aren't you?'

'Right, New York. I'm Ray. Pleased to meet you.'

He looked as though he meant it, and held out his hand.

'Joe. Glad to be here.'

Ray opened a new bottle of wine and poured me a full glass, also pouring a double whisky for himself.

'I open at eight, but people don't start arriving until ten. Hang around and you'll have plenty of company, some you might have heard of.'

I expressed an admiration for the antiques and the tasteful décor.

'Yes, you see when I first came here, I opened as a gallery selling antiques and paintings, and did fairly well. I had a good clientele and I always offered them a drink, but I found that I was giving out more drinks than I was taking dollars, so I decided to turn it into a bar and charge for the drinks, and let the customers look at the antiques. I've never looked back since. I do make exceptions though, so that one is on the house.'

'I do like that painting,' I said, pointing to the picture of a young man.

'Yes, I could have sold that over again, but I never would. I knew the young man; he was a very good friend,' and, looking at the painting, added nostalgically, 'and lover.'

I got to know Ray very well during that first visit to Portugal and we later developed a close friendship, but he did not attract me sexually and his appetite for sexual encounters was directed elsewhere. We sunbathed together on the rocks, visited Lisbon and nearby towns and villages and dined and entertained at his flat, often with Charles, his long-standing partner. Charles, although in his seventies, or because of it, had a collection of young Portuguese men who seemed to depend on him. He also collected Meissen porcelain, on which he was an authority, and traded in it in the USA.

Ray and Charles had been lovers, but time or temptation had eroded their sexual attraction for each other, and given them the freedom to look elsewhere for sexual partners. Ray had worked in advertising in New York, had found it too competitive and, with Charles, had come to Europe to live. They had surveyed Venice, Marbella and Lisbon to set up a business, before deciding on the more tranquil resort of Monte Estoril. They had made the right decision as it was an élitist resort with a world-renowned golf course and casino, and attracted many celebrities and big spenders.

By ten o'clock, Ray had been joined by a Portuguese barman, and more people were arriving. They were obviously affluent, worldly sophisticates, all apparently known to Ray and respectful towards him. One man, who stood out from the drinkers, engaged me in conversation.

'Are you a friend of Ray's?' he asked.

'I've just met him.'

'Oh, he's a fine man, a lovely person,' he said with a Spanish accent. 'I'm from the Hotel El Sol, manager. You should be staying there.'

I assured him that I was happy where I was.

'Got to get back,' he said. 'I've got some big American golfers to look after, including Bing Crosby. It's their last night.'

The place was busy now, with a buzz and an excitement that inhibited me from leaving. Ray and his bartender were kept busy, but Ray kept up a familiar chat with everyone, never without a whisky by his side.

It must have been midnight when I decided that I had drunk enough and was taking my leave of Ray, when the manager of the El Sol returned. He faced Ray.

'Look what Bing Crosby gave me,' he said disapprovingly, holding up a camera.

'It looks a good camera to me,' said Ray.

'But I can't work it! I can't work it!'

With that, he threw it onto the floor and jumped on it in fury. People were aghast, but others who knew his temperament, laughed and applauded.

Ray had a preference for local fishermen with whom he made friends on the beach, and at night there were always two or three of them outside his bar waiting for him to lock up, which he did at one or two o'clock in the morning. Ray would then drive with them into Lisbon to drink and listen to fado singers. True to the Portuguese melancholic character, the fishermen would often be overcome by the emotion of the fado singer. One, Antonio, a twenty-year-old, who was known to have been the lover of the El Sol manager, threatened to kill himself when he found out the manager had been unfaithful to him, with another man. The fact that the manager was married seemed immaterial to him, which I later found unsurprising as most of the fishermen who were looking for sex were married.

Ray would rarely return home before four o'clock in the morning, and then sleep until midday. I made many subsequent visits to Ray over several years, during which he often proposed that I join him in running the bar, saying that there was enough income coming in for both of us. It was tempting, but I knew that the bonhomie necessary for running a bar, the late nights, and the habitual drinking were not for me. Running a bar was not the wisest business for an alcoholic to be in and Ray eventually succumbed to cirrhosis of the liver and died in Lisbon. Most of the fishermen of Estoril and some from the nearby resort of Cascais turned up at his funeral, and many of them wept at their loss.

— Thirty-One —

MAKING ADVANCES

Putting the thoughts of a life abroad onto the back burner, I faced up to the reality of continuing with Woolworths. After all, there were the advantages of secure employment, good salary and a pension at sixty, none to be given up lightly. My experience had given me the knowledge of store management and I was looked upon favourably by top management for further promotion. As it happened I did not have long to wait.

My return to reality coincided with that of another manager, who also returned from holiday, but was confronted with a store he no longer felt capable of running. He was older than me, not in good health, and he asked for, and was given, early retirement. I thought of the similarities of our situations, but with our differing responses to them. I rather envied him the age difference that made his departure possible. The store was in the mining, workaday town of Nuneaton, Warwickshire, known to me only as a railway junction I had occasionally passed through on train journeys and immediately forgotten.

'I want you to take over Nuneaton on Monday!' ordered the managing director.

I had been summoned to the district office, reassured the director that I was the right man for the job, received a slap on the back, departed with his good wishes, and a warning that it would not be an easy store to run.

Relocating a manager was quicker with single men than with married men, because of fewer family commitments and with cheaper relocation costs to the Company. It benefited the Company and aided my promotion. I could still pack all my belongings into one suitcase, although now I had a car to put it in. It was 1963, and Woolworths was the main store in the town, with Tesco and Sainsbury yet to arrive. The store was too small for the volume of trade it attracted and was situated on a corner, hemmed in by roads, which prevented expansion. A larger store was planned, but it was still on the drawing board. It was not long before I realised why the previous manager had decided on early retirement. The constraints of the outdated building tested any efficient management and, without decent staff facilities and with full employment in the town, recruiting staff was difficult.

The staff and ancillary rooms of the store were on the first floor and only accessible by a spiral staircase or, in emergency, by a meandering corridor through the stockroom to the goods lift. Staff going down the staircase had to give way to other staff coming up. Tea breaks stretched out from the permitted fifteen minutes to twenty minutes, and longer, as staff waited to ascend or descend. Tempers frayed, particularly mine, as staff breaks overran and customers' frustration grew. Staff members who took ill either had to recuperate in an overcrowded staff room, or suffer the ignominy of being carried feet first down the spiral staircase or in the goods lift. This happened with unsurprising frequency as my predecessor, with admirable motives, believed in employing more disabled people than the store quota demanded, resulting in disabled people making up most of the workforce.

Staff struggled in to work, sometimes only to sign in, before resting and apologising that they were unfit to work or to make the ascent up the spiral staircase. An offer to use the goods lift was usually declined as discourteous. If they were 'feeling poorly', it was best if they remained on the sales floor, and sat down to rest.

'Can I go home, please? I'm not feeling well.'

How many times, I wondered, would I hear that plea, sometimes before I had even opened the store?

The cramped conditions throughout the store were not conducive to retaining even fit staff and the consequent staff turnover made managing the store a daily challenge. The staff supervisor, a Mrs Harkness, defended her engagement of staff.

'Only the disabled would work here anyway, because they have difficulty getting work anywhere else,' she said.

'Don't take any more on, anyway,' I responded, 'We need fit people to work here.'

Her look of disapproval, which she had worn since my arrival, hardened.

'I was born in this town and I know people don't take kindly to shop work.'

'Well, we will up the pay,' I said, adding as an afterthought, 'If necessary.'

Her look sufficed to deflate any hope I had of support.

'Now, do you know of anywhere I might look for accommodation?' I asked.

'No, I don't know of anywhere.'

After staying in the only hotel in the town, I again needed permanent accommodation, so I looked in the local weekly newspaper, where an advert for a 'Paying Guest' looked promising. At least it sounded better than a 'boarder', and so it proved. I became the only paying guest to a widow, a Mrs Goodall, in her sixties, who really only wanted a man about the house for the added security, she said. Her husband had been a bookmaker, and she had a very comfortable home, which she was happy to share with me. She was also another very good cook, and pandered to my tastes.

'I am having a group from my church here tonight,' she said one morning, looking at me hopefully. 'Would you like to join us?'

'No, thank you, I'm not really into religion. I will be out anyway.'

She was a lovely, thoughtful, kind person, and despite her

regular religious meetings, I soon relaxed into the comfort and hospitality she showed me. Unfortunately, it was not for long, as six months later she suddenly died of heart failure.

Her sister, Mrs Allbright, who I had met, phoned me at the store to tell me the unexpected sad news, and also to offer me temporary accommodation with her, should I wish it. Accepting her considerate offer, I packed my suitcase again and moved in.

'We don't have the comfortable home my sister had – after all she married a bookie – but we would like you to make it your home for as long as you wish.'

Her husband was a retired local government official, and she had a son, Gilbert, an outstanding scholar and articulate young man who was waiting to go to Cambridge University, and a daughter, Elizabeth, who worked in administration at Leicester University. Elizabeth was at home infrequently, and I felt she was not totally comfortable with me. While listening to an LP put on by her classical music loving brother, I would catch her looking at me intently, before blushing and looking away.

Later, I received an unexpected letter from Elizabeth confiding that her friendship towards me had grown into something more, and before she could see me again, she needed to know if I felt any love for her. If I did not, I was not to respond to her letter, and she would not refer to her feelings again. As I felt no more than friendship towards her, I did as she asked, and did not reply. I was surprised that she had not perceived my true inclinations, as I showed more interest in her brother than in her.

I had only been with the Allbrights for three weeks when a lady introduced herself to me in the store and expressed regret at the sudden death of Mrs Goodall, who she knew as a friend.

'If you are looking for accommodation, my sister is looking for someone respectable, and I knew that Mrs

Goodall thought highly of you.'

At her invitation, I went to see her sister, who again turned out to be another elderly widow, unable to live without 'a man about the house,' and I agreed to move in.

I began to ask myself if this was going to be my life; the comforter of doting widows? I took too easily to their home cooking, and their attendance to my wants and comforts. Perhaps it was time to find my own place and to look after myself but, for now, I needed all my time managing the store.

Work had began on building the new Woolworths and preparation had to be made for relocating, transferring stock, and engaging staff, whilst continuing to run the existing store. Sainsbury and Tesco were now opening simultaneously in the town, and we all competed for scarce staff. The innovation of self-service was being introduced into the town by the new competition and, although it was not welcomed by everyone, it quickly caught on. Counter service, which Woolworths continued to give was costly, less efficient and belonged to a passing age. Nevertheless, with our head in the sand, we were building a new store to incorporate it.

'Take on whoever is suitable, whether disabled or not. With no spiral staircase in the new store it will be easier,' I said.

'Well, with Sainsbury and Tesco opening up they won't be queuing up to join us will they?' was the staff supervisor's response.

The building progressed until 1964 when we opened the store to the acclaim of the local newspaper's endorsement that we had not 'gone over to the impersonal self-service system, which the public dislike and are unlikely to accept.' How wrong could they be? Time would tell.

— THIRTY-TWO —

ON THE ROAD

With a new modern Woolworths store in a prime location and with better staff facilities, staff morale improved overnight. Previously sour-faced, complaining assistants discovered how to smile and actually enjoy their work. It brought home to me that given the right conditions, attitudes can be changed. Managing the store became much easier and more rewarding. One day a visiting executive put an unexpected question to me.

'Do you see yourself progressing beyond store management?'

Promotion was in the offing, but they had to know that I would not turn it down if they offered it. Saving face was as endemic in the Company culture as it is in the Japanese. I knew intuitively that my response now would determine my future.

'Yes, as far as I can go,' I said, showing a confidence I did not feel.

The next rung on the ladder, after store management, was as area manager; being responsible for a group of twelve to fifteen stores, as an intermediary between stores and executive. It usually meant packing a bag every Monday morning and driving off to the stores wherever in the country they were situated, staying in hotels, and driving back on a Friday night. It was not a prospect which married men enjoyed, but most accepted it as they were ambitious and married more to their jobs than their wives anyway. The relative freedom from routine, the travelling, and the absence of the boundary of four walls appealed to me, also with the prospect of the road leading eventually to London.

I did not have long to wait before promotion came. A year after opening the new store in Nuneaton I was appointed area manager of a group of stores in Yorkshire and was 'on the road'. I was troubleshooter and pacifier, confidant and antagonist, responsible for store operation and on standby for whatever emergency or dispute arose. Not only had I to establish the trust of the store managers, but also report on them, enforce the company policy, and be aware of their shortcomings, infidelities and strengths.

Although it was never accepted Company policy, some managers saw fit to increase product selling prices to cover for pilferage loss, known in the trade as 'shrinkage'. Surprise store visits were more likely to reveal shadier practices. On one such visit I found an extra cash register in use, the contents of which went to the manager. On another store visit, after finding the cash balance short by two hundred pounds and confronting the manager, he admitted to 'borrowing it'. Exposing the manager caught in such dishonesty would result in his instant dismissal. I did not report it, although not reporting it was tantamount to condoning it. Knowing a manager, his lifestyle and circumstances, meant that I could not feel detached. I felt the responsibility keenly. Most of the managers were loyal and honest. They had come into the company and worked their way up from the stockroom, as everyone had from the chairman down, motivated by financial reward, and with egos matching their aspirations. Self-effacement was considered a shortcoming, but there were exceptions.

One such exception was Archie, a manager of a small store, who carried humility to the extreme. Archie was overwhelmingly considerate to his all female staff and customers alike, and was a popular and respected figure in the town. He was a tall stick of a man, droll, hesitant, with a timid smile, not overtly homosexual, but nevertheless his mannerisms and sympathetic nature had already marked him in the company as questionable. I was told that he was not destined to progress to a larger store, the comment being made that 'he was just unsuitable', despite the fact that he ran a good store. When I had established his confidence, he acknowledged that he was 'inclined that way', but had no active experience. I felt an affinity with Archie and would have wished to come out to him but thought better of it for fear of him passing on the information.

I knew of no manager or executive who had 'come out' but, by the law of averages, and with over a thousand managers, there must have been more than a few in the closet. I knew it would be unwise to be open as, at the very least, I would have been shunned and any promotion would have been blocked. Homosexuality was illegal in practice, with the business world more intolerant of open homosexuality than in many other walks of life, and Woolworths was no exception.

Heterosexual relationships prospered within the Company and, whether illicit or not, were commonplace. Most directors, executives and store managers married women employees they had befriended in their store days, but their loyalties to their wives were stretched as they progressed up the ladder. With secretaries kowtowing to their whims and advances, romantic liaisons tested many marriages. Although women greatly outnumbered men in the company it was a totally male-dominated business. No woman was on the board or held an executive position. Directors rose through the company and seniority amongst them determined who was next in line for managing director and then chairman. The procedure ensured 'jobs for the boys' and maintained the status quo.

Nepotism was fostered from the chairman downwards, and fathers, godfathers and uncles in the business ensured that any male relatives were given a helping hand up the ladder. Of course it was all done discreetly but family names and connections often gave the game away, even when confidences did not. Staff relations were good by the standards of the day, and loyalty and long service were the expectation. Managers were also highly incentivised as they were paid on a percentage of the profit their store made. The percentage was reviewed whenever a manager moved to another store. The expansion of the Company to over a thousand stores, and its recognised high profitability and dominance on the high street, had attracted more young men to become trainee managers. But their ambitious expectations were not always fulfilled and some got tired of the long wait and sought their fortunes elsewhere.

One such was Richard Kirk who founded the retail clothing chain of Peacocks Ltd. Another was Malcolm Walker, who at twenty-four had futilely waited seven years to be a manager, before going out on a limb and opening a shop in Shropshire selling loose frozen food. A more far-sighted board of directors would have acknowledged his initiative, seen the potential of his concept, and backed it financially. Instead, two months later, when they found out, they fired him. His enterprise prospered and evolved into Iceland Foods, making him a multimillionaire.

I did have thoughts of striking out on my own but was too intent on the job I had to realise them. My work had too many challenges to be boring and there was satisfaction in solving the many problems which arose in store operation and management and I was doing a job I liked. I was also feeling a loyalty to the Company, and saw further progress ahead of me. Why give it up? Yes, my sexuality was constrained but that did not stop me finding outlets for it outside of work, often finding opportunities because of the necessity of travelling between stores and staying in hotels.

It was in one such hotel in Cambridgeshire, close to an American base, that I met a black American, Paul, with whom I struck up a conversation. He was dressed in civilian clothing and it was not until I had got his confidence that he told me he was a sergeant in the American army. In a further test of my confidence he admitted being gay, after I came out to him, and that he wanted an 'English experience'. I was very attracted to him. He was young, handsome, solicitous and very caring as I was to find out when he accepted my invitation to spend the night with me.

We had both fallen for each other and met whenever we could arrange it, eventually holidaying together in London, Amsterdam and Cornwall. There were few black people in England in 1965 but Paul was surprised at the absence of prejudice he encountered compared to his experiences in the USA and even amongst the soldiers on his base.

'You English are so nice and so well-mannered. I would love to live here,' he often said.

Six months into our relationship, Paul was posted back to the USA, promising to return after his service expired. Our separation was eased a little by frequent correspondence and phone calls until he was discharged from the army and went to live in San Francisco. The following year I joined him there on holiday and found the gay life to be rife with promiscuity and abandonment. Not only in the gay scene but also among the hippies and flower power movement which was taking root in the city. I soon discovered that Paul was caught up in a more promiscuous gay lifestyle that did not accord with our vowed commitment to each other. He would have liked to have returned to England with me and said that if he did he would be faithful, but I had seen enough to suspect otherwise, and could not agree. The flame of love had been extinguished by exposure to the permissive wind blowing through San Francisco.

We had an intermittent correspondence over the following years during which he expressed his love for me and his continuing desire to live in England, but as I could not return his love I held out no helping hand. Letters diminished into exchanging Christmas cards and in his last card sent to me in 1982 he wrote that he was ill with pneumonia. This coincided with the outbreak of aids in San Francisco and, of course, aroused my suspicions that his illness was more than pneumonia, but it was not until 1986 when I visited my brother Alf in San Diego that I was able to confirm that Paul had died in 1983.

— THIRTY-THREE —

REMEMBER ME

Hitchhiking was prevalent in the nineteen sixties and, feeling the need for company when often driving to long-distant stores, I would sometimes succumb to the outstretched arm. Usually there would be a line of hopefuls, young men, sometimes students, waiting at the junction to a motorway. Some would display a board showing their destination, their expressions taking on a look of anticipation as I slowed down to pick up the most interesting or least objectionable. Some days, not wanting company, I ignored their mute entreaties and, driving on, saw their momentary hopes evaporate, leaving me with a pang of guilt. Far better to pick out the most desirable companion and with pointed finger indicate my choice.

That was how Rodney entered my life. He looked the most interesting, with red hair, strong features and a cheerful expression.

'Where to?' I asked, winding down the window.

'York if possible or as near as you are going, please'.

Well-mannered anyway, I thought. Sometimes it was unwise to divulge one's final destination, then if the hitchhiker turned out to be unsociable or boring, he could be dropped off earlier.

'I'll see how we get on. Get in'.

He smiled with satisfaction as he eased himself into the adjacent seat, and drew a sigh of relief.

'Thought I would never get a lift today'.

'Do you do this often?'

'No, I don't usually travel far from York.'

Looks about twenty-five, I thought, and not a student.

'I'm Rodney Blades, Rod to my friends.'

'Live in York?' I asked.

'Yes, live and work there, but I was born just outside. Long Marston, near Marston Moor actually. Have you heard of it?'

No, I had not.

'Big battle there in 1644, in the English Civil War. Oliver Cromwell and all that. Four thousand men killed there in one day. You can still find bones and shot.'

'Interesting history lesson,' I commented. 'So what do you do then?'

'I'm a builder when I'm working,' he added, 'which is not now. Are you in business?'

I saw that Rodney was a confident and engaging young man. 'Woolworths, actually'.

He looked surprised.

'Not with all those women?'

'Not really. Administrative.'

'My mother used to work there, years ago.'

'Do you see much of your mother then?'

'No, not really, only when I need cheering up, or been in a spot of bother.'

Further disclosure revealed that 'a spot of bother' meant a brush with the law, resulting from street fights.

'You seem a nice guy. I bet you've never been up before the Magistrates,' he said.

'No, public disorder doesn't appeal to me.'

'Nor me neither. It's just that I'm known in York, and get confronted.'

'Who by?'

'Oh, straight chaps, who know me.'

'What do you mean, straight chaps?'

'You know, straight, as opposed to bent.'

'What, you mean you are queer?'

'Yes, can't you see it?'

'No, can you see it in me?' I asked.

He looked at me and smiled.

'Well, I thought you might be, otherwise I would not have come out to you.'

He slowly laid a hand on my thigh and settled back into the seat.

So I had made the right choice from the queue, I thought. York suddenly became more interesting. I dropped Rodney on the outskirts of the city at a bus stop at his insistence, but not before we had arranged to meet in the lounge of the hotel I was staying in that night.

When he entered the lounge he was spruced up in a tweed suit, a fresh glow on his face, his eyes taking in the room, then lighting on me. I felt a thrill as he entered.

'Hello Joe. This is new to me. I've only been in the public bar.'

'Well, I'm sure the drinks are the same. They just cost more here, but if you would rather be in the public bar ...?'

'No, this suits you, doesn't it?'

Rodney told me of his background. A tearaway as early as ten, when his father left home. Playing truant and getting into street fights and being knifed as a teenager, resulting in a spell in hospital with a collapsed lung. There, he proudly told me, he had learnt embroidery.

'I still do it, except I'm better at it now.'

I looked at his hands; builder's hands, rough and red, and had difficulty in imagining those fingers doing anything as dexterous as embroidery, but I was yet to know how sensitive a young man he was.

We had our first night together that night in the hotel bedroom, and in guiltless acquiescence, found satisfaction and reassurance in each other.

Next evening we met in a pub of Rodney's choice. There he was amongst friends, but they left us to ourselves, except one who Rodney introduced as 'Sue', his flatmate. He was young, blond, and camp.

'I hear you are coming to our place tonight, dearie,' he said.

'Oh really? Rodney never said.'

'It was meant to be a surprise,' said Rodney. 'You will come, won't you?'

'Yes, I would love to.'

'I hope you know what you are letting yourself in for,' quipped Sue. 'But I won't be there to see it.'

My second night with Rodney reaffirmed our mutual attraction. The flat looked more of a squat, with wall hangings of provocative slogans, the union jack, male nudes and couplings. There was a double mattress on the floor.

'Is this where you both sleep?' I asked.

The answer was obvious, but I needed to know the implications.

'Yes, but we don't have it off. He doesn't turn me on at all. We are friends, that's all. It's just convenient. Anyway, Sue isn't often here, she has other friends.'

Business took me away from York next morning, when I bade farewell to Rodney, and agreed to meet up on my return. We then met again at his flat, and agreed to walk into town to the same pub. Rodney had a jaunty walk and, as we walked, I noticed he looked at people rather intensely, as if expecting a reaction or as if he knew them. I supposed that if you had lived all of your life in one town, then you come to feel part of it, but Rodney walked more as if he owned it.

I noticed two youths walking by on the other side of the road looking at us and laughing.

'Poofs,' one cried out.

Like a bullet just fired, Rodney was across the road, and

with flaying arms, wrestled the youth to the ground. I crossed over and, pleading with them, pulled them apart. The youth had got the worst of the encounter and seemed relieved at my intervention.

'Does this happen very often?' I asked, after Rodney had dusted himself down and we resumed our walk.

'No. Well, occasionally, but as you can see, I can take care of them, so I don't get much trouble.'

I then thought of what my own predicament would be if anyone from the store had seen me. Rodney was obviously known in the town, but probably only in his own circle. I took comfort in the fact that he was not outrageously gay. He looked what he was, a working class lad with no pretensions, and that is what appealed to me.

I met Rodney on most of my visits to York, but some nights I had work to do, or went out drinking with the store manager, when I always avoided the streets near Rodney's favoured pub. He did not have access to the phone so I arranged to meet him in advance.

'I don't see you often enough,' he said on one of our meetings. 'Why can't I travel with you?'

'You would have nothing to do all day. Now you've got your job. Anyway it wouldn't be possible.'

He put on a sullen look, but it was not for long.

'I tell you what,' I said, 'I'm in Bradford next week. Why not join me there, in the hotel, for a couple of nights?'

Rodney instantly perked up and happily agreed.

He was waiting for me in the hotel lobby when I arrived the following week and accompanied me to my room.

Inside, Rodney embraced me, and said, 'I've missed you.'

'I've missed you too.' I said in all honesty.

He then gave me a small parcel he had been carrying.

'It's for you, to remember me by,' he said wistfully.

Opening the parcel revealed a linen tablecloth, beautifully

embroidered with sprays of flowers. Embroidered on one corner was an entwined monogram of our initials. I was stirred by the seeming incongruity of the tough outward appearance that Rodney put on and the sensitiveness and openness which he showed in our relationship and felt humbled by it.

'Rodney, how lovely, but you are not going away, are you?'

'Hopefully not, but who knows what the future holds?'

I had ordered a twin-bedded room, so no eyebrows were raised when, on our way to the dining room, I booked Rodney in.

The delights of Bradford, if any, did not entice us out those two nights. Our delights were found in each other, and the hotel walls ensured our privacy.

It was another two weeks before I visited York again, and after a day's work in the store, I called at Rod's flat. He was looking downcast and embraced me rather hesitatingly. I hugged him.

'What's the matter?' I asked.

'I've been charged,' he said with a hangdog expression.

Causing an affray again, I thought, rather unkindly.

'What for?'

'Gross indecency. I was in a toilet and another man made a pass at me and I was tempted. Turned out he was a policeman. Enticement.'

'So what were you doing?' I asked.

'Just having a wank,' he said, 'Didn't even fancy the policeman.'

'I'm so sorry,' was all I could say.

'It could be a prison sentence,' he said. 'They've been to the flat as well. Sue was interviewed, too. You had better not come again. You may be seen and then they could accuse us of being a homosexual ring or something. They interrogated me, trying to find out who I was in contact with, but I didn't tell them about you. I didn't have your address anyway, and it's best if I don't have it, otherwise you could be fingered.'

As he spoke, I became increasingly anxious.

'Hold on, aren't you being a bit alarmist? How do they know we are not just friends?'

'Oh, they could easily make a case against us. How we met … you picking me up … you coming here … me staying with you in the hotel … Sue. Even seen talking to some other queers in York could be used against me.'

Yes, I thought, it could all add up to whatever they wanted.

'What can I do?' I asked. 'Can I pay for legal representation for you?'

'No, that would only strengthen their case, if they found out you were paying. Anyway, I can answer for myself. I was provoked. *Agent provocateur*, don't they call it? I may get off,' he said without conviction.

I embraced him and held him in my arms for a long time.

'I'm sorry,' he said. 'I had hopes for us. I always mess things up. I didn't have to tell you, but if I don't see you again, you'll know why.'

And I did not see him again. When I called at the flat on my next visit, it was empty and no one in the house knew of their address or the circumstances of their departure. I went to the pub that Rod had taken me to and asked there.

'He's been sent down for six months for gross indecency,' I was told.

'And Sue? Do you know where he is?' I asked.

'Sue's gone to Leeds.'

Either because of the pressure of work or a disinclination to entangle myself with the prison system and the inevitable questioning of our relationship with untoward consequences, I made no attempt to find out which prison Rod was in to enable me to visit him, which I later regretted. Perhaps it was the realisation that it was the end of a relationship which was doomed anyway.

Now, when I have visitors to afternoon tea and they notice the monogram, I feel remorse if they ask who RB was.

'A young friend I unfortunately lost touch with.'

— THIRTY-FOUR —

A SALUTARY ENOUNTER

Travelling between stores and being 'on the road', as it was known in the company, appealed to my sense of independence and free spirit, unrestrained by four walls and the responsibility of managing a store. During the working week, hotel life supplied my bodily comforts, and Nellie, my Nuneaton landlady, pandered to my wants at weekends. I was in an enviable position. Nellie was a generous woman, both in size and character. A comforter and home maker, with only me, like an adopted son, to smother with her kindness. Her home, a whitewashed cottage called the 'The Little Nook', with its long front and back gardens, set back from the road leading out of the town, known as 'The Long Shoot', became my home too.

Nellie had two married sons living in the town who between them ran the family quarry business, but their first responsibility was to their wives, one of whom was aspirational, with the other more content with life. John, the eldest son, with the contented wife, had recently purchased one of the largest houses in town for the then record local price of £10,000. It was 1966 and the house price boom had not yet taken off. The 'aspirational' wife, married to the younger son, was consumed with jealousy. They lived in a modest semi on an estate.

'Why could you not have bought it?' became her perpetual recrimination against her husband.

'He's too slow to get ahead,' she would say, turning to me. 'You've done well, haven't you? And you haven't got a woman behind you! You have the field to yourself. Isn't that what they say?'

She was constantly trying to draw me out of my natural reserve, her curiosity about my single status never satisfied. She would have liked to put the question of why I had never married to me, but avoided doing so. To do so, would have been indiscreet of her, and requiring a direct answer. Her familiarity would go as far as, 'I bet there is a girlfriend somewhere,' but discretion on my part kept confirmation of the truth from her, and I relished her unsated curiosity. When a man is in his thirties, unmarried, with no obvious girl friend, putting two and two together can only add up to four, but the question usually remained unasked – unless one was of the ilk of Larry Grayson, and then there was no need for the question.

Grayson was a local camp comedian, and in later years, after he had become famous on television, he moved into the 'Long Shoot' with Fan, the daughter of his adoptive mother, who brought him up. In 1966 he was unknown outside Nuneaton and the Midland's working men's clubs, where he performed as a drag queen and also as a stand-up comedian. I first encountered him in the Woolworths store at the cosmetic counter with three men, of similar physique, tall and slim, where they were testing the colour of lipsticks on the back of their hands and then putting them back on the display. The lipsticks were for sale, not for testing. I went up to them.

'Do you mind not doing that? There's a test card there.'

Larry's mouth turned up at the corners into a smile as he looked benignly at me, and then, pursing his lips together, with a gesture that was to become his hallmark, he threw his head back, before turning to his companions and saying, 'Oh, get her!'

With that retort they all turned round, briefly held their noses, and then grandly walked out. A supervisor came up to me.

'You know they're local performers? They are on at the Miners' Club. Drag queens.'

'Well, that doesn't give them the right to spoil the lipsticks. Other people will be buying them.'

In later years, I got to know Larry as the kind, likeable, generous person he was and several times saw him perform on stage. Nellie, my landlady loved him. Unfortunately he reinforced the prevailing heterosexual perception of a gay man; waspish, camp and limp-wristed, but it was natural to him and I still liked him.

I continued to relieve the mediocrity of Midlands life by travelling to London for weekends and, when holidays allowed it, abroad. My favoured London base was a small hotel in St Martins Lane, off Trafalgar Square, so convenient for the clubs, saunas and theatres of the West End. I was given a key to the front door when staying there, to come and go as I wished. Nearby was 'The Salisbury' pub, a favoured haunt of stage artists and the gay fraternity, which I would frequently visit after the theatre. It had a Parisian air about it, original art nouveau décor and lighting, with etched mirrors all round the walls. One could relax in the comfortable padded leather seats; forget time and the world outside.

On one visit I took up my preferred seat at the bar, near the door, where I could look along the length of the bar and view the bohemian clients which the pub attracted.

A young man came and sat next to me, obviously alone and not one I had seen before, and ordered a pint of Watneys.

'Not very busy tonight, is it?' he said, his eyes wandering around the room.

'Yes, not too crowded, either,' I said. 'I like that.'

'No actors in either', he said, seemingly disappointed. 'That's unusual. They like this place.'

'So, who have you seen here then?' I asked, more to keep up the conversation, than out of interest.

'Well, Elizabeth Taylor and Richard Burton were here last week.'

'Really? That does surprise me. Did you see them, then?'

'Na, but I wouldn't 'ave minded.'

I liked his answer. I would not have minded myself.

'Nice place though, isn't it?' I said to maintain the conversation. 'Cigarette?'

He turned to accept the cigarette, and I saw that he was younger than I first thought, perhaps only eighteen. He had dark eyes which, when they were not lowered, looking at my crotch, were half hidden by his long black straggly hair.

'Yes, I suppose it is. Haven't seen you here before. Visiting are you?'

'Yes, I'm staying down the road.'

'That's convenient,' he said. 'Where're you from?'

We passed an hour away in conversation, and I learnt that he was from the east end, and had an unhappy childhood until his father had died. 'Bastard, he was.' He was happier now that there were only his mother and two brothers.

'Aren't you going to invite me back?' he asked with an ingratiating smile.

The thought had entered my mind, and it was obvious from his expression that he thought I was taking a long time to ask, so putting doubt aside, I conceded, and we left the pub together. Nothing much was said as we made our way to the hotel, and my thoughts were on the sexual possibilities which lay ahead.

In the dark, I fumbled for the keyhole, while he stood behind me, pressing his body against me. My anticipation and sexual arousal intensified as we climbed the stairs. I silently opened my bedroom door and motioned him to come in. No sooner was he in the room and I had closed the door, than he pulled out a knife, confronted me with it, and said, 'Empty your pockets or I'll let you have it.'

'If this is a game, I don't like it', I said, putting on a firmness I did not feel.

'It's no game, mate. It's your money or your life!'

I made for the door, but he caught my head in the crook

of his arm, and held the knife against my throat.

'Give me your wallet now, or else.' His voice was unequivocal.

'I'll give you all I've got if you let go.' I preferred my life to the fifty odd pounds I had on me.

He relaxed his hold, and while he still pointed the knife at me, I took out my wallet and handed him all the notes I had. He grabbed at them, and then unexpectedly struck me on the head and ran out, while I lay writhing on the floor. As sadomasochism held no appeal to me, I derived no pleasure from this attack. Neither could I go to the police to report the assault, as I would have been open to the more serious charge of procuring for underage sex, if my attacker was, in fact, under twenty-one, as well as a charge of gross indecency. On reflection, I felt foolish, and that I had got my just deserts.

— Thirty-Five —

A LONG WEEKEND

1967 saw the legalising of homosexual acts between consenting adults in private. Before then, loving a person of the same sex could make you a criminal. Looking twice at someone in a toilet could lead to an arrest, and being in the wrong address book could lead to prosecution of being in a homosexual ring.

It was estimated that one in twenty men were homosexual and various theories were disseminated. Opinions varied from 'being born that way', an unhappy childhood, fathers not showing affection, to possessive or overprotective mothers. Homosexuals often chose to cover up their predilection out of fear of criminal charge, being ostracised by friends and family and at work, or being blackmailed. Many took on the cloak of marriage in the hope that it would change them or conceal their true inclinations.

The only openly gay man in the Woolworths head office employing some hundred men was Rodger on reception, who was the butt of jokes, innuendo and ridicule. To do my job I had to have the respect of the managers and management. I knew of the entrenched homophobic attitude in the company, from boardroom down and a change in the law had not altered it.

For me, it was not until 1973 when a sequence of events changed my life. London had its attractions, and even a knife at my throat had not diminished them, but the nearby city of Birmingham held out a more welcoming hand. I found it in gay clubs, and in one in particular, The Grosvenor on the Hagley Road, owned and queened over by a youth-besotted host I knew only as Gerald. I too was attracted to younger men, but only one at a time, whilst he had a coterie of them and, being the owner of the establishment, used his position to retain them.

One evening I was approached for a dance by one of his circle, who introduced himself as David. As we danced together, I felt an immediate rapport with him, and one dance followed another, interspersed with drinks at the bar. Gerald stood at the bar, giving me black looks, which became darker as the night progressed. David then said he had better be getting back to his boyfriend.

'Oh, I didn't know,' I said crestfallen.

'Yes, he gets very jealous if I dance too long with anyone else.'

'It's not Gerald, surely, is it?'

'You mean Mother? Oh no! Not her! I'll see you next time. You're a lovely dancer.'

With his promise and compliment I decided that was as much as I could expect that night and left the club. As I was getting into my car, I was grabbed by my shoulders from behind and swung round. Immediately a fist landed on my face.

'Keep off David, you cunt. He's mine.'

I grappled with my assailant and exchanged blows before two other guys separated us.

On later visits to the club, both David and I kept our distance from each other, he probably out of concern for me, and I because someone more important came into my life.

It was some days later when a friend named Malcolm approached me, and, speaking softly said, 'There's someone who is dying to meet you.'

'Really, who?'

'He's a friend called John, living in Aberystwyth.'

'How does he know me then?'

'He comes to Birmingham sometimes because his mother lives here, and he's seen you in here, but he hasn't liked to approach you.'

'That's my usual effect on people. Tell me about him.'

'He lived in Birmingham before going to Aberystwyth with his partner, Steve. Steve has a hairdressing business there, and John learnt hairdressing from him.'

'So, he's a ladies hairdresser then?' I said, my interest rather diminishing.

'Yes, but he's not camp. Quite the opposite really, and good looking.'

'You sound like a matchmaker,' I said.

'Yes, that's been said before, but it's not worked for myself.'

I knew that Malcolm had suffered violence from his partner and had endured it out of misplaced love. He had not known a father in his childhood and I suspected that his partner, who was a much older man, was a father figure for him.

He said that if I was interested in seeing John he would tell him and arrange a meeting in two weeks' time, but I gave it little thought in the meantime. When I then entered the club, Malcolm was standing with a handsome, dark haired, moustached young man of about thirty years old.

'Hello, Joe, I would like you to meet John.'

John smiled expectantly at me as we shook hands, his eyes alert to my response.

'Thanks for coming,' he said with apparent conviction.

I looked at John and felt I had known him forever. His warm brown eyes, willing me to like him, burned into mine awaiting my response.

'I'm very pleased to meet you. So how is Aberystwyth then?'

'Very isolated and dull,' he said.

'Well, I'm sorry for you. I have never been there, so I'll take your word for it.'

'I will leave you two to get to know each other,' Malcolm

said with a grin and excused himself.

John and I soon found ourselves immersed in each other's opinions and experiences, and I felt very comfortable and at ease with him. He was much more of an extrovert than me, with a ready laugh and relaxed manner. I knew that I had to see more of him.

'Would you like to meet up again? I can be here next weekend,' he said, voicing my thoughts.

The next weekend came none too quickly, when we met again at the club, and immediately resumed our intimacy. John told me that he was not happy in his relationship with Steve.

'I was in one before,' he volunteered. 'But that was with a woman. It lasted four years, too. I even got to the altar and at the last minute I took fright and called it off. I was trying to be normal and my family expected it, but it suddenly hit me that I was not being true to myself.'

He invited me to visit him in Aberystwyth the following weekend.

'Is Steve agreeable?' I asked.

'Oh yes, I've told him about you and he would like to meet you. You can stay overnight.'

'If you are sure,' I ventured. 'Tell me about Steve.'

'Oh, he's ten years older than me, and it's his own hairdressing business. He's good at it too. He introduced me to it. I have him to thank for that, but not much else.'

I met Steve the next weekend when I drove to Aberystwyth. The town looked attractive with its castle ruins, its seafront and two sand-swept bays. I could see nothing dull about it, and, on meeting John, I asked him why he had said it was.

'It's very isolated and hemmed in by the mountains. I find it very depressing, and the people are very parochial.'

'You've been happy here these last four years,' said Steve, posturing with arms akimbo.

'I wouldn't say that. Only some of the time.'

Steve's face darkened, and, looking at me ruefully, he said, 'He does change, you know. He changed his surname from Meads to Burns.'

I thought it malicious of Steve to divulge this information to me and that, if John had wanted me to know, he would have told me in his own good time. The revelation did nothing to lighten the cloud which I felt had descended since I arrived.

'Why did you do that?' I asked John.

'Because of my father. I didn't want to carry his name. He sexually abused me when I was a child and my sisters too.'

'That's all in the past,' said Steve. 'Like so much else. You're a big boy now but you still can't take care of yourself.'

'What do you mean?' asked John.

'You would be lost without me.'

'Oh! Don't be too sure of that.'

Steve continued to put John in an unfavourable light, presumably for my enlightenment. I felt that I had unwittingly become the third side of a triangle about to crack.

That evening we went out for dinner and the demeaning repartee from Steve continued, with John increasingly affected. Steve saw the mutual attraction John and I had for each other and understandably resented it. On returning to the house, I asked John where I was sleeping that night.

'With me of course,' he said, quizzically raising his eyebrows.

'And what about Steve? Surely he minds?'

'He's agreed. He doesn't mind.'

I doubted it, but the arrangement was not beyond my expectation. Out of an unspoken consideration for Steve, we did not have sex that night. It was sufficient to lie in each other's arms.

Next morning, John awoke and said, 'I will bring some tea up.'

When he went down I heard Steve's voice raised in acrimony, before John returned, shaking in anger.

'Steve wants me to leave. Says he's finished with me. And I've finished with him.'

The crack had opened up sooner than I had expected and I had precipitated it, or had I been set up? I felt I was the fuse by which an explosive charge had been ignited.

Steve avoided me that morning. I would have liked to apologise for coming between him and John, but no palliatives from me would have been acceptable or alleviated the rift now. Events were gathering a momentum of their own and carrying me along with them. When I had been invited for the weekend I had not foreseen the consequences. There is no telling the outcome when emotions take over. Perhaps a time for reflection had come.

'Let's go out and talk things over,' I suggested to John. 'Hasty decisions are not usually the best ones.'

'It's not a hasty decision. It's been brewing a long time. We just don't get along anymore. I don't love him and he doesn't love me.'

'And I'm the catalyst?'

'Maybe but you are more than that to me now. I've fallen for you.'

'And me for you.'

We walked along the deserted promenade with a cold wind blowing off the Irish Sea. The mountains enclosing the town, with its castle ruins, gave it a brooding, ominous look. Then the rain clouds gathered and the sky darkened. It should not be like this I thought, even now out of season; the sun should be shining down on us, but instead the rain came, and we ran for shelter.

Alone in the shelter we embraced and huddled together looking out to the grey black sea, and the sea horses riding the waves. John had warned me he was impulsive.

'When I get something into my head it drives me crazy unless I do something about it.'

John had been born and raised in Limerick, until his mother separated from his father because of his ill-treatment of the children, when she brought all five of them to Birmingham. His voice still had the southern Irish softness and warmth.

I thought of the fourteen-year age difference between us, and the protective feeling I had for John, but it was more than that. I felt at ease with him and an awakening love which was more than the physical attraction that had brought me here. I too could be impulsive.

'Come back with me, today.'

As I said the words I knew that my life would be changed. It was not just an offer of help, but an invitation to share the future.

'Would that be possible?' asked John.

'Yes, I'm sure. I'll ring my landlady and let her know I'm bringing a friend back, but first we must settle things with Steve.'

On our return to the house, John was anxious about our reception, and he was immediately confronted by Steve, who turned on him with vehemence.

'This is the end of our road together so you had better pack your things.'

'Can we shake on that?' asked John, but Steve turned his back on us and left the room.

'Well, that's that then. I'll just get my things. It won't take long. I want to get away.'

'I'll wait for you in the car. Take your time.' I said to John.

I sat in the car and lit a cigarette to relax my mind. I asked myself, was I acting in haste, being drawn down a road I had not intended to travel, only to have regrets later? Was it love, and what is love? It has to be a physical attraction first, surely? We certainly had that for each other. Perhaps wanting to be together and feeling affection for another person was enough? I did feel that way, but it was more than that. Yes, it was love, but love brought with it a responsibility, and I felt that too.

Half an hour later, John came out with his bags and a suitcase.

'Let's be off. I want to put Aberystwyth and Steve behind me.'

'Well, you mustn't be too hard on him. It's all been a bit sudden.'

'He's only taken back everything he gave me, including my watch.'

'So he's feeling vindictive? That's not surprising.'

There was only one road out of Aberystwyth and we took it.

As the wet slate roofs of the town disappeared behind us, John's spirits lifted and his smile and humour returned.

'I'm so glad all that is behind me. You are the best thing that's ever happened to me. You'll never regret it.'

'You know I have never lived with a man before? I've never met one I wanted to live with.' I said. 'Now I have, and I think it's love.'

I was already feeling a release from the constraints of my past. Now I could look forward to coming out to the world and to myself, being in a relationship to face the world and a future together, and I was feeling happy and relaxed about it.

At the first village with a telephone kiosk, I phoned Nellie, my landlady, and asked if I could bring a friend back to stay a while.

'Where will he sleep?' was her first response.

'He'll have to share my bed. It *is* a double.'

'Well if you're happy with that, I don't mind at all. He will be very welcome.'

Nellie lived up to her promise and quickly took to John, whose natural familiarity and humour ingratiated him to her. She had already brought up two sons, and caring for two men came naturally to her. But we knew that, while expedient, the situation was not one for two gay lovers, the double bed not withstanding. We agreed to get our life together in our own place and decided to set about looking for it in Birmingham.

Nellie's eyes brimmed with tears when we told her of our intentions to move out when we had found somewhere.

'I suppose it's only natural. No one will fill your place,' she said, looking at me. 'It's been seven years.'

And no one did fill my place. Nellie was in her late seventies and in the following year she sold her house and moved into a care home, but she was not one to sit and be looked after. She preferred to keep busy and do as much caring as the staff allowed her to. On several subsequent visits to see her, I found her busy in the kitchen or assisting in minding less able inmates until, two years later, she became too frail herself. No longer able to help others, her purpose in life diminished, and within a few months she died in the home.

— THIRTY-SIX —

THE WONDER OF WOOLWORTHS

I was in the fortunate position of being able to put cash down on a flat. Never the big spender, and having lived most of my life in digs, my spending habits could be described as frugal. I had invested my savings in the stock market but the untimely stock market crash of 1973 wiped out most of my capital. The shares which were of value, and I was able to sell, delivered £12,000 which bought a new flat off the Hagley Road, in Birmingham, not far from the gay club where I had met John.

My last remaining shares were sold at a further loss to furnish the flat, but the choosing and buying of the flat and furniture now gave me more pleasure than being a shareholder. We bought into the new contemporary style then emerging, chrome and leather settees and chairs, mahogany veneered wall units, fitted carpets, recessed lighting, glass-topped tables, and the all important stereo and LP player.

At last I was free from the constraints of living in other people's houses and adapting to a landlady's expectations. Having a choice was liberating for us both. I was beginning to realise that a relationship was more than one plus one, but a multiplication of caring and sharing common interests with a coming together of the emotional needs of each person.

'You know that Virgo and Capricorn are good for each other?' John said with some conviction.

'That's reassuring.'

But I did not need astrology to endorse what I knew in my heart. I liked being part of a couple and now knew that was what I had always wanted.

‘I think it’s time we threw a house-warming party,’ suggested John. ‘We’ve been here all of two weeks and friends are asking.’

‘I suppose so.’

My heart sank as I imagined the new carpet being spoiled by spilt wine, dancing in the crowded rooms, and neighbours complaining of the noise. None of which turned out to be true except that the wine ran out, and there was little room to dance with twenty guests celebrating our good fortune.

Music and dancing were intrinsic to John’s personality, which made our visits to the nearby gay club more frequent, and I had to accept that there were better dancers there than me, and younger ones, waiting to dance with John. I was not jealous, only happy to see him lose himself in the rhythm and movement. We soon built up a music collection of our own. I got to appreciate Elvis, Queen, Diana Ross, David Bowie, Johnny Mathis, but their music competed with my preference for soul, Nina Simone, Sam Cooke, and Roberta Flack. Fortunately we came together on our tastes in music as in so much else.

‘Who does the cooking?’ asked a newly acquired neighbour.

‘We are still working that one out. I believe if you can read you can cook, and there are plenty of books on cooking.’

With my life having been lived in hotels and digs, with food provided, I was very much a stranger to cooking, and John was easy-going about it. Eventually beef stroganoff and roast lamb became my signature dishes and John made chilli con carne his.

John lost no time in getting a ‘chair’ in a hairdressing salon and soon built up a clientele. He was a natural draw to women, quick to establish a rapport with them, good-looking, friendly, humorous, and engaging to talk to. I knew all this but it was confirmed, not only from his colleagues, but also from some of his clients who became friends of us both. He found being openly gay was an advantage at work and I envied him that. It could not have been more opposite to my own experience. The more open he was about it, the more his personality and popularity shone through.

No work associates of mine had been invited to the house-warming party as I continued to keep my private life discreet. There was little social rendezvous at work anyway. 'Not fitting in' at work was really no problem for me, as there was no social structure to 'fit into'. I had moved up another rung of the ladder into an administrative desk job, in yet another layer of middle management. It was 1973, the year of the three-day week, pay freeze, strikes, fuel rationing, and IRA bombings, but I kept my head down, got on with my job and thought how lucky I was.

The recession continued into 1974 but hardly impinged on John and me. We continued to entertain, take holidays abroad, became habitués at the Grosvenor gay club, took up squash, and on Sundays walked the Clent Hills, and on some summer days, joined in gay picnics there. Our lives were settling into a routine when in 1975 I was unexpectedly summoned to London for an interview with the chairman who offered me an executive position at head office. John was enthusiastic at the prospect of moving to London, but I was apprehensive. I felt at home in Birmingham and amongst friends.

'Of course I don't have to take the offer. It means selling up and leaving our friends, and you finding another job,' I protested.

'That won't be a problem. I can do my work anywhere. Our friends can always visit and we shouldn't have a problem selling the flat.'

But we did. There had been a collapse in the housing market and it was three months before we sold. During the weekdays I stayed in the Victory Services Club in London, a modest but comfortable ex-service men's club near Hyde

Park, and went back home at weekends. John was not happy staying on his own during the week and our haste to move to London precipitated selling the flat at a loss. But at least the sale of the flat gave me the money for a deposit on a house in London.

Erroneously thinking I knew London from previous visits I soon discovered the limits of my knowledge when I trekked the suburbs looking at properties which I usually found fell short of the agents' descriptions or revealed undesirable features. In these early days of the introduction of the postcode I still thought that its sole purpose was for automating the sorting of mail and, in my ignorance born of the provinces, gave little thought to it. Why should SW1 be more desirable than EC1 or W3 less desirable than W5? I soon found that the postcode now not only determined the location but also the property values, insurance costs, attractiveness and the social mix of the area.

John would have been happy to live anywhere in London, but I wanted a garden and on my budget that meant the suburbs, so why not go to the 'Queen of the Suburbs', Ealing, W5 with its easy access to central London and the recently opened M40 to the Midlands? Searching estate agents' windows, I saw a photo of a 'secluded two-bedroomed town house in a desirable road'. In haste and weary of searching further, I put in an offer, £500 below the asking price of £18,000, with barely a second look. It escaped our notice that it had a flat roof, a shared drive, faced north, was shaded by adjacent buildings, was badly built, and being 'of unusual construction', was not looked upon favourably by mortgage lenders. Nevertheless it felt right. We liked the appearance of it and, as it had a garden and French windows, and John was now desperate to join me in London, we signed the contracts and moved in as quickly as we could.

No sooner had we moved to London, unpacked, laid the carpet, hung the curtains, and put up the beds, than our entourage of Birmingham friends descended on us for the weekend expecting an impromptu house-warming party. Wine and passing around a few innocuous joints was all that was needed to rise to the occasion, with enough floor space for slumberous bodies to recline.

Gay friends quickly acquired nicknames, usually feminine. That weekend I was bestowed with my 'tag' of Lucy when I was seen mopping up a spillage, using a newly acquired mop bucket labelled 'Lucy'. John was already known as 'Scarlet', earned by his infatuation with Vivien Leigh as Scarlet O'Hara, and her character's part-Irish ancestry, although some friends joked that it was more to do with the film's title *Gone With The Wind*, as John was known to break wind at inappropriate times, and cause much mirth.

John's mother, Kathy, lost no time in visiting us, and insisted on being shown round London, much of which was a revelation to us as to her. It was possible for the public to walk into Downing Street, even to stand on the steps of Number Ten and be photographed, which we thought would be the highlight of Kathy's day. We were wrong. The highlight came five minutes later when, walking along Whitehall, she found a £20 note on the pavement.

'It is true then? London is paved with gold! I'm going to move down and live with you.'

'No you're not,' retorted John.

Within the first two weeks of our move to London, John had set about creating a garden from the grass plot attached to the house, and dug out a ton of earth to make a patio alongside the house, before thinking of looking for a job.

'Start at the top and work down the list.' I advised. 'Isn't Vidal Sassoon top notch?'

'Maybe, but they only employ stylists who they've trained at their academies. No, I'll try Harrods first.'

John had misgivings about applying to such a high profile store, but at his interview and the test they gave him, he managed to overcome his nervousness, and started work there the following week. He quickly found his confidence in his new environment and soon established himself and built up an appreciative clientele.

Meanwhile I was trying to find my way into the Woolworths executive conclave and establish my role there. Retailing had become more challenging with supermarkets making inroads into what had been traditional Woolworths trade. We were still market leaders in sweets, records and DIY, but new ranges had to be found. It was decided to expand into ladies and men's clothing on a much larger scale than we had done before.

I was very sceptical of Woolworths being an attractive fashion label but, despite my misgivings, I was put into its promotion. Many managers and staff shared my doubts on this move into clothing but, whatever reservations I had, it was my job to allay their scepticism and implement the company policy. To introduce the clothing ranges into the stores, it was decided to present fashion shows in countrywide venues, and I again found myself on the road travelling between stores, organising staff and setting up the shows in provincial towns.

Despite not having 'come out' at work, I suspect that my dress sense and fastidiousness had not gone unnoticed. After all, I had raised a few eyebrows returning from a holiday in Venice wearing a silk suit, and had I not first flouted the company's unwritten rule, that only white shirts were to be worn? But there were other signals which I was giving out, which only the deaf and blind could not have noticed. I made no amorous advances towards women employees. I showed an interest in the arts and theatre and none in sport. I had a reticence to join in heterosexual male bonding and the boasting of sexual conquests. In fact, my sexuality was an open book, but not one given a voice.

An ambitious TV advertising launch was started in 1975

which dominated the television screens with well paid celebrities endorsing the new company slogan, 'That's the Wonder of Woolworths' and was a huge, but expensive, success. Customer inflow into the stores increased, and sales rocketed, but it was achieved at the expense of reduced profit margins and costs of the campaign. Eventually Woolworths followed the strategy of the USA parent company and started looking outwards for acquisitions. It was the policy in the States to sell and leaseback Woolworth stores to finance the acquisitions, but in the UK, freeholds were as sacrosanct as the crown jewels. Nevertheless, the more conservative members of the board were overruled, and expediency and the UK's biggest shareholder, Woolworth USA (with 52% of the shares) dictated the sale of the larger store freeholds to finance suitable takeovers.

The first major acquisition was B&Q, then an emerging DIY retailer, followed by Superdrug, Comet, and MVC music specialists. The sale of more stores and freeholds financed the expansion of these acquisitions. This began another era for the company, with many highs and lows, eventually leading to being taken over itself, and its subsequent decline.

Despite the success of the advertising campaign, the drive into the clothing market proved a mistake and was quietly run down by the company except for children's clothing. I moved into the buying of household textiles, where, again, further expansion was planned, which meant overseas visits to Hong Kong, China, Turkey and Portugal on buying trips as well as visits to UK factories. Although these trips took me away from London, John was always glad when I returned. He was too much of an extrovert to be happy on his own. Now with my job based in London and a home I could say 'ahhh' to when I returned, I looked forward to a shared and more settled lifestyle with the man I loved.

— Thirty-Seven —

THE DREAM

By the following year, 1976, London had become our world. We no longer felt like stranded strangers fresh from the provinces. We knew our way around the clubs, galleries and pubs, and had sorted out which welcomed gays. Some were exclusively gay, as was the 'Colherne', the haunt of the leather crowd in Earls Court, and the 'Quebec', off Oxford Street, known as the 'Elephant's Graveyard', because its habitués were older men whose followers, the gerontophiles, patronised them, either for sex or their money. Other bars were appropriated by gays only on certain days. The 'Markham Arms', on the King's Road, attracted the Chelsea gays on Saturday lunchtimes, and the 'Horse and Groom' in Belgravia, where on Sundays, off duty guardsmen mingled with the Ra Ra Ruperts and the Hooray Henrys.

New gay venues were opening up, many with discos and late licensing laws. Too late for my enjoyment or for getting up for work next day, but for John, dancing until three o'clock in the morning was a self-indulgence. I would lie awake at night waiting for his return, anxious that he may have had an accident. Twice he crashed the car, fortunately not seriously, but being a company car, and to get it repaired, I had to claim the accidents as mine, which led to questions about my driving ability. Lying awake brought on other concerns. Who was he dancing with and what else did he get up to? Why was he happy to go out on his own until so late at night? Was he looking for sex with someone else? Was dancing the only drug or was he into a more insidious one?

His reassurances to me that it was only the dancing that kept him out so late were not always convincing, but I was ready to believe him, and was not going to restrict his natural disposition. A caged bird is not a happy one, and anyway, how could I doubt his love when he declared it to me so often?

It was a long hot summer, with the parks filled with bare-shouldered women and bare-chested men languidly sunbathing. There was a drought and a hosepipe ban had been declared, with even a Minister of Drought being appointed by the government. By now we had laid out the garden borders and planted them, carrying buckets of water daily to keep the plants alive, and put our final touches to home improvements with a summer house, a new kitchen and an extension. I was feeling that it had all come together for us, and there was no reason for it not to continue.

We had an overgrown bushy honeysuckle growing on the garden wall and we found a cat had given birth to kittens in it. John took one kitten out of the litter and brought it into the house. The mother followed him but we never saw her after that, so we kept Kitty.

'Why don't we get a dog, as well?' asked John. 'I've always wanted one. It need only be small.'

That weekend we went to the Battersea Dogs Home, to start our search, and a red-haired Irish terrier jumped up at John, nuzzling into his hand.

'It's not us choosing the dog, it's the dog choosing us.'

Miss Kitty and Kelley soon established an acceptance of each other and, to all appearances, completed our domesticity.

'It's amazing who you see when you're walking in London,' John said one day in Chelsea. 'Did you see who that was? Alan Bates, the actor, and he made eye contact with me. I'm sure he's gay. The way he looked at me gave me the feeling that he wanted to speak.'

'That's probably the last thing that actors want, strangers speaking to them. It must happen all the time,' I said.

It was strange, I thought, as only ten minutes earlier, a black guy had also looked at John with a half-concealed look of recognition. John had averted his eyes, but his face had coloured, as if in embarrassment. I felt reluctant to comment because of my suspicion that they knew each other, but I wondered why, if they did, John had not acknowledged him? I kept my silence, but John's reaction weighed on my mind for days afterwards.

The longer John worked in Knightsbridge and the more he knew of London, the more disenchanted he became with living in a quiet, middle class, family orientated suburb, where there was little social interaction, and no gay venues. I was happy with the relative solitude and quietness, and after a day's work looked forward to driving home to the leafy suburb and putting central London behind me.

'I'm fed up of travelling to work by tube,' he said one day. 'I would love to get a motorbike. It doesn't have to be a Harley Davidson.'

I agreed that a motorbike was just what he needed and when he got it, it soon became his fourth love, after me, Miss Kitty and Kelley, until another love came into his life.

'You know I've always wanted to travel,' John said.

No, I did not know. I thought we were happily settled.

'Well you haven't done too badly this year. We've been to Italy and Morocco. You mean around the country on your bike?'

'No, I mean abroad. I would love to go to America and work there for a year.'

Another dream of John's, I thought, one that will stay a dream.

Then one evening, late in the year when the days to Christmas were being counted by children and shopkeepers, John came home from work.

'I've been offered a job in Copenhagen with an international company. A three-month contract, starting in

January, with a chance of a transfer to the USA after a year, with all expenses paid.'

A lot of questions came into my mind. Had the offer just come out of the blue? Why Denmark? Why now? Why at all?

'It's a bit sudden, isn't it?'

'It's a chance to travel before I get any older and regret not doing what I wanted to do. I know I will miss you, but I can come back after three months. I do love you and I know you'll understand.'

He told me that I was the best thing that had ever happened to him and that I had given him the confidence to do something he had always wanted to do. Three months is not long, I thought, and he'll be glad to get back. Being alone in a foreign country would soon diminish his enthusiasm. I knew I could talk him out of it if I tried, but would I want to live with the guilt of having killed a dream?

'Then you must do it, and I'll be waiting for your return.'

The year turned the corner into 1977 and after the activity and the farewells to friends, the day of his departure arrived. I felt an emptiness and a sense of loss when I saw him off on his motorbike, and a regret that I had acquiesced to the separation.

A day after arriving in Copenhagen, John wrote, 'I feel so homesick and lovesick for you. How could I leave you?' He continued to write every week. 'My life is empty without you. I love you very much and miss you even more.'

He was disillusioned with Denmark, finding it extremely cold, very expensive, and his work associates superficial. Eventually, in March, we were both looking forward to his return at Easter.

'All I want is to come home to you and be happy again,' he wrote.

Easter arrived, but not John. Another letter arrived instead saying that he had decided to go to Berlin for Easter.

'Just to see it, before coming back home. I know you will

understand.'

Yes, I understood that he was impulsive, wanted to travel, and that he needed more excitement after his moribund experience in Copenhagen. Why not, when Berlin was so accessible and so uniquely interesting? It was still a divided city, with a wall between the affluent west with its liberated lifestyle, and the communist east, and I could understand John's interest in wanting to visit it. But would he be alone in Berlin? He had not said where he would be staying or who with. Had he already met someone? I threw all doubts aside, and put our reunion on hold, knowing it would not go cold.

John's next letter gave me another but more questionable surprise as he asked me to 'try to understand him a little longer'. He wrote that he was captivated by Berlin and would like to stay and get a job and a flat there.

'One day I will settle down and it will be with you. In the meantime, forgive me for being so selfish.'

Perhaps I did understand, but it did not ease the separation which now seemed to be without end. Perhaps it was the end, and we were not prepared to face up to it? Possibly he was having an affair, but to avoid hurting my feelings, would not admit it. Or was he stringing me along and keeping his options open?

I reflected on our four years' living together. I suddenly realised it was four years that John had lived with Steve in Aberystwyth, and before then, he had a relationship with a woman for four years. Was he living his life in four year cycles? Were four years the limit before a relationship lost its meaning? I recalled Steve saying to John, 'You've been happy here these four years.'

Now I found myself in Steve's position.

'He does change, you know,' Steve had said, as if warning me.

How true. It all came back to me, but this was different. Now I was the one who had been left behind in John's search for himself. With my encouragement John had found the freedom and confidence to live his life on his own terms and I could not blame him for that.

Being John, no sooner had he arrived in Berlin than he met a fellow traveller dipping into its alluring nightlife. Wolfgang was visiting from Hanover, and there was a mutual attraction. John was quickly enamoured, and immediately moved in to live with his new-found friend.

I realised that it was the end of our relationship when I received his letter.

'I love him very much, and I will be staying in Germany, but I will always have you in my heart.'

Yes, John, I thought, but no heart is big enough for two loves and you have broken mine. I felt an emptiness inside me. While we had been apart I had lived for our reunion, but John had been as impulsive as ever and followed his emotions.

Despite feeling let down but out of continuing friendship, I maintained a less regular correspondence and soon John asked if he could visit me and bring Wolfgang. I agreed and it was then, when I saw them together in an embrace, that I knew the reality of their love for each other. I again felt that my heart had been wrenched from me and I could not contain my tears. Was it jealousy or self-pity? Whatever it was, I was aware that a period of my life was over. Although I had fostered the thought that John would return one day to spend our lives together, I would be deceiving myself to maintain that hope. I would have to move on. John already had.

— Thirty-Eight —

BORN AGAIN

Now that my relationship with John had unravelled, I began to realise the freedom of being single. My work at Woolworths continued but was now enhanced by the overseas buying trips instead of the troubleshooting visits I used to have to make to provincial Company stores. Doubts and disillusion were behind me and now I was answerable only to myself.

I went into a phase of self-improvement. After all, I thought, what better investment could one make than in oneself? And so I took up Hatha Yoga which promised a calming of the mind through relaxation, meditation, and physical postures. Although centuries old in India, it was just making inroads in England in 1977. Being the only man in a group of twelve women was not an unusual situation for me. The equivalent male/female proportion was the same in the watercolour and music appreciation classes I also enrolled in. Was it only the females of society who felt the need to improve themselves?

In anticipation of a new experience, I unrolled my yoga mat, and sat squat, stood on my head, or balanced on my shoulders. In between, I attempted the various postures; the plough, bow, cobra, crow, fish, camel, wheel, foetus, and the auspicious, although not all at the same time, while I tried to regulate my breathing, and looked in vain for the aura surrounding my instructor, which she assured me, would become visible. Getting into the postures and maintaining them was an achievement, but they failed to lead to the calming of the mind that was promised. The exhortations to empty the mind just seemed to create more space in mine for mundane matters, fears and worries. Inducements to 'stay with it', 'let it flow naturally', or 'feel the calm', had little effect. Perhaps I was trying too hard, but I did stay with it.

It was the instructor who gave up first, and left the class without direction, eventually to be disbanded. One permanent benefit which I did achieve through yoga was inducing myself to give up smoking.

With several of the more persevering women, we underwent a metamorphosis and joined the only other alternative group around, which happened to be in Ayurveda. This enabled us to continue with our yoga and meditation, but required us to balance our food intake between the 'elemental energies', or humours, of wind, bile and phlegm, or in Hindu, vata, meaning air and space, pitta, fire and water, and kapha, water and earth.

Being told that I had too much kapha, was no surprise to me. I knew that my fondness for potatoes would find me out. I needed more vata, and as I was already almost a vegetarian, I just needed to increase my intake of salads to get my metabolic system in balance. It was the strictures to eat only the food in season which did it for me. I mean, when is it the season for bananas? I knew when garden peas and beans were harvested, but to restrict one's intake of them to the early summer months, was asking too much, and I was not going to get rid of the freezer. I could possibly see some justification for eating only foods in season in an agrarian culture, but not in the UK which imported most of its food, besides I was not overweight or suffering from any known illness, and neither did I want to suffer from malnutrition. I needed to look elsewhere for enlightenment.

I was going to more concerts, plays, art galleries and operas than I ever had in my previous forty eight years of life, usually alone, but quite liking my freedom from attachments. After seeing a performance, I began revisiting an old watering hole, a discreet gay club called Napoleon's. So discreet you could miss it if you did not know it was there; up a side alley off Bond Street. Its clientele were mainly discreet too, professional, early thirties and upwards, with many from overseas.

On coming down the stairs, I passed a young Asian-looking man, whose large and expressive eyes caught mine. We met later at the bar, and he introduced himself as Theo, a pharmacist from Indonesia.

'Oh, Java?' I asked tentatively.

'Well it is Java actually, but it could be Sumatra, Bali, Borneo, or a thousand other islands. They all make up Indonesia you know and some other islands too, but anyway, I'm living and working in Germany for now.'

Yes, he's Javanese, I reflected; coffee brown skin, wide open eyes, small stature. I conjured him up in Indonesian dress; Batik shirt, black hat, perhaps a sarong.

'Yes,' I said weakly at the thought. 'Interesting, and how do you like London?'

'This is my first visit. I only came for two nights, from Marburg in Germany, to see "The Sound of Music".'

'What, on your own?'

'No, I brought two elderly German ladies with me. We are staying at the Lillie Hotel.'

I could imagine him being attractive to ladies as well as to men. He had a caring charm about him.

'And where have you left the two German *Fraus*?' I asked with a hint of irony.

'In the hotel. They will probably be asleep now. They've had a long day.'

'And so have you,' I replied, reflecting that he was young, early thirties, and obviously with the stamina to stay awake all night, which is what happened when I invited him back home.

His charges saw little of him that weekend before he escorted them back to Germany. We knew we had to see more of each other and all the following year we oscillated between Marburg and London, until Theo moved to London to live with me for six months, the maximum time permitted on his visa. Such was the beginning of a lifelong relationship, and a life changing one too.

I soon found out that Theo was a devout Christian, and a regular churchgoer. He had no sooner moved in with me than he started going to the parish church and then persuaded me to accompany him. I complied more out of friendship than faith. The vicar, Richard Hayes, welcomed me, and then, to my embarrassment, introduced me from the pulpit to the congregation. I felt a transgressor amongst the serious elderly worshippers turning round, smiling and looking at me expectantly from their pews.

Richard was a cultured, charismatic, enthusiastic vicar of my own age, and we soon became friends. Theo volunteered his services as a Sunday school teacher and was also welcomed into the choir, both of which he had experience of in Germany and Java. Richard soon asked me to fill a vacancy on the Church Council, and from that, I was asked to become secretary of the PCC (Parochial Church Council). Meetings and minute taking, jumble sales and coffee mornings, driving spinsters and widows to church and back, church maintenance and finance now began filling my diary and spare time.

Soon I was making weekly prison visits to Wormwood Scrubs and conversing with criminals and murderers, praying with them, and for them. I thought I was on a spiritual journey and felt that I was being virtuous. Because of my implicit conversion to religion, Theo believed he had saved me from damnation. What had started as a gesture to a friend had become an integral part of my life. Having been a sceptic, I was now being drawn into discussing theology and church practice, and thought that my enlightenment had come.

Theo's six-month visa expired and he returned to Jakarta where I joined him for a month and was readily accepted by his family who were active church members. The Anglican minister of the 'English' church, an Australian, welcomed me and introduced me to the diverse congregation. The church service was followed by 'English' tea on the lawn and I found myself surrounded by well-wishers, expats, and native Javanese, all eager to welcome me into their church. Their enthusiasm was no less muted when they learnt that I was only visiting.

Returning back home I began to question the value of prayer with Richard and discussed the bible's teaching. It puzzled me that, being an intellectual person, he could have such a closed mind on his belief and faith. Faith to him was implicit, not something to be questioned. For me, it was as much an intellectual journey as an emotional one, made more intense by the solemnity and theatre of the Eucharist service. Richard then suggested that I join him and another priest in a weekend retreat in Kent and I readily accepted. We sat through the weekend in silence, except at meal times and at prayers. Mostly I prayed alone in my little room, praying for an increase in my faith and for forgiveness for my sins, the top of the list being my homosexuality. Although it was only a weekend of contemplation and prayer I was drowning in a flood of emotion. I felt, or convinced myself, that I was being saved, and assured myself that my new-found faith was giving meaning to my life.

On my return home I read the bible more assiduously, increased my attendance at church, prayed more earnestly, doubled my giving and engaged in the church services with renewed vigor. To assuage my guilt and to remove possible temptation, I destroyed all the literature, pictures and photos of a homosexual nature which I had collected over the years.

I was now ready to believe I was a born-again Christian and decided to confirm it. At the age of thirteen I had started confirmation instruction, only to have it curtailed when the vicar molested me and I fled from the church. Now, thirty five years later I was to finish the instruction. Who says that years give you wisdom? I received confirmation by the Bishop of London, and deluded myself that I was on course on my spiritual journey.

The delusion was short-lived and like a romantic love affair, too fragile to last. The more I engaged in the church activities the more I found was expected of me, urged on by the weekly appeals from the pulpit to 'increase our giving', and Richard's own commitment and personal exhortations to me. I began to see the church as no more than an institution which preserved vested interests. Adherents professed a faith, usually without question, but for most, church was a social service that alleviated their conscience, where they could feel reassured and comfortable with like-minded people and assurance of life after death.

Two unconnected events brought my attachment to the church to an end. One was the departure of the vicar, Richard, to another parish, and the other was reading the newly published book by Richard Dawkins, *The Selfish Gene*. This convinced me of the scientific explanation of life by natural selection, and demolished any remnants of belief in 'creation' or a supernatural deity. Looking back, I could see that I had been caught in an emotional wave which had tossed me on its crest and now had stranded me on the shore, but I had not drowned. I had come ashore on firm land and felt sure of my footing.

Now I could put my religious past behind me, and with it, the feeling of guilt. I accepted my homosexuality as an inherent part of myself, not something to be ashamed of and rooted out. Unsurprisingly, friendships I had made at the church ended when I ceased going to church. Theo believed and probably prayed that I would return to the faith and maintained his friendship. Having been indoctrinated since birth in his beliefs, he hung onto them. His Christian faith had been fought for by his family over generations, against the majority faith of Islam, and he was obdurate in holding on to it. To him, Christ's teaching of love included both sexes and deviants and homosexuals were not outcasts.

Other changes in my life were afoot when in 1982 the first rumblings of a change in the fortunes of Woolworths were heralded. The parent American company agreed to sell its 52% shareholding to a consortium of London city financiers. The newly appointed chairman immediately called a meeting, announced a radical overhaul of the company, and told us that it was now the year one, and however many years we had served up to then, they counted for nothing. Suddenly loyalty was a spent currency.

Nevertheless, new challenges had to be faced, and I stayed on to implement some of the new policies, but by 1985, the writing was on the wall and disillusion finally set in. I did not last as a born-again Woolworths man any more than I did as a born-again Christian, and having completed thirty-five years, I decided to retire and at the early age of fifty-five, to take up my pension rights.

I immediately took off to join Theo in Jakarta, and together we travelled through Java, Sumatra and Bali. I was intoxicated with the relaxed lifestyle and welcoming attitudes I found on our travels and seriously considered taking up residence, or at least a second home, on one of the islands, perhaps Bali? But to be with Theo, it would first have to be Jakarta, and he agreed to look for a congenial property where we could have a second home. Good residential properties were available from £10,000 which I gave him to buy a house as soon as he had found one suitable.

Six months after my return to the UK Theo wrote and surprised me by announcing that he had met a young lady of Chinese ancestry at his church who he was thinking of marrying. Could he use the money to buy a house for them which I could also live in? And would I be his best man? It was not the news I was expecting as he had never before mentioned that he wanted to marry, but I reasoned that being back in his own culture, and amongst his family, he felt a need to conform. He also wanted his own family, and showed a love of children with his Sunday school classes. I knew that our sexual relationship had ended but I saw our friendship continuing and I agreed to his proposition, although I saw little likelihood of me sharing the marital home.

I returned to Jakarta three months later with a pair of Chinese antique vases as my wedding present, and with the approval of his bride, to fulfill my role as best man. With some two hundred other wedding guests I joined in the celebrations at the Hilton Hotel before seeing off the newly-weds on their honeymoon to California. Theo and his wife bought their house but later moved to Sydney, where Theo established his own pharmacy practice and where I joined them in 1988 for a holiday and for the christening of their son, Mark. I agreed to be a witness, as in all honesty I could not commit myself to the Christian vows required to be godfather, although Theo still held out hopes of my reconversion and continued to pray for my salvation.

— THIRTY-NINE —

PHOENIX

'Welcome to the 1992 seminar of Insight. My name is Martha and I am your facilitator. We are going to ask you to participate in your experience and experience your participation.'

Well, that sounds clever, I thought, but was it not just gobbledygook? I was in Bloomsbury, London, in a hotel ballroom, but I was not dancing ... yet ... but standing with fifty-nine men and women of every age, class and colour, nervously fingering their name badges and looking around for reassurance. Having failed to find myself through religion, yoga, or extended periods of travel, I had cast cynicism aside, and enrolled in a programme of self-awareness. We were promised a 'positive and profound experience' and had high expectations but were not sure of what.

Martha was on the platform, a self-assured, attractive brunette, thirty-something, with a voice assuming caring Californian sincerity.

'Before we start the sharing, let's go over the ground rules for the seminar. You'll hear them a lot this week, but begin using them NOW! They are:

'Use everything for my advancement,

'Take care of myself so that I can help take care of others,

'Don't hurt myself and don't hurt others.'

I was taken back to my all too brief Boy Scout days, and the scouts' promise, and almost put my hand across my chest as I silently recited the 'rules'.

'We recommend honestly sharing the REAL YOU, and enthusiastically moving towards your dreams. DOING DOES

IT!' continued Martha.

Now I even doubted my rebuttal of my cynicism and, as I looked around the participants, caught the eye of a Latin-looking young man, who, with a look of forbearance, smiled at me. Perhaps the 'sharing' *was* already beginning to work. I was to find out over the next six days that 'sharing' meant opening out to other people, signalling for a roaming microphone and then proclaiming one's thoughts, feelings, opinions, or confessions to the group.

Early 'sharings' were largely innocuous, feeling the way and testing the parameters of group participation.

'I feel uplifted by the energy in this room. Does anyone share it?' someone at the back said.

Hands went up and it seemed that everyone did, or claimed they did.

As the morning progressed and more hands went up, confessions became more personal.

'I feel unloved by my partner.'

Don't we all, I thought; anyway be lucky you have one.

'I prejudge people in a negative way, before I even know them. Does anyone share this with me?'

Well, I could say, I would not wish to be negative, but judging yourself can be very negative too.

Next, we were asked to move around the room and stand face to face with as many individuals as possible, saying to them one of three statements:

'I am willing to be open with you,' 'I am not willing to be open with you', or 'I am not willing to say which.'

I moved around facing as many people as I could, 'willing to be open' and getting the same response from them. The Latin-looking man got to me before I could get to him and, facing me, said, 'Are you coming out with me?'

'I don't think that's the question you're meant to put. Do you mean "coming out to me", or are you "coming out" and you want me to "come out" with you?'

'Whichever way you like,' he said with a very pronounced Italian accent. 'English is very confusing.'

I left the question unanswered, and moved on. It was too early in the seminar to form attachments.

We then divided into groups of three to five and recounted our past; voicing our individual fears, our inadequacies, our feelings of being unloved, and the restrictions we put upon ourselves. Discovering that these weaknesses were shared seemingly by everyone in the room gave us the confidence to open up more. By the third day I was ready to get onto the platform and come out to the group by announcing that I was homosexual. I received a resounding round of applause and people surged forward to embrace and congratulate me as if I had just won a race, or saved a life. I felt my approval rating rocket, but I was not sure if I had deserved it just by being honest with a group of strangers.

Then, more as a challenge, I turned to the least gay-looking man in the group, an Asian, who I noticed had done more 'sharing' with the women and did not appear to engage with the men. He introduced himself as Sanjay, and although a Hindu, appeared formal and conventional-looking. He congratulated me on my 'coming out' but was hesitant about his own sexuality, and showed more interest in my experiences than in divulging his. My first observations were confirmed when he confided in me that he had often been rebuffed socially by white men and he always felt safer with women. Although he admitted that he was sexually attracted to men, he had never given in to the feeling or even spoken of it before. He was twenty-nine years old, half my age and, I suspected, sexually repressed. And then I thought of John, who was also twenty-nine when I first met him, but far from being sexually inhibited. Did I have a predilection for men of that age, I wondered, or just younger men in general?

'I could not come out to my family. Anyway, I'm not sure

if I am homosexual,' Sanjay was saying.

'Perhaps having some experience of it may help you to decide,' I suggested. But he did not take up the implicit invitation, and instead started telling me of his family background and childhood in Bombay. I pictured a middle class Indian family, English by virtue of their domicile but keeping to their Indian tradition and mores.

'You should get out more. Lose your inhibitions.'

I liked giving advice that I could not always take myself.

'You are right,' he said, 'But I don't have the courage.'

'You showed courage coming here, but you have only started. I'll help you along the way, if you like. Think, what else have you done to break the mould?'

'I did a parachute jump once. Does that count?' he asked.

'Oh, definitely. I could never do that. Why not take the microphone and share your feelings with the group? You'll find it very empowering. Doing does it.'

I was beginning to speak the jargon.

'No, not yet. I'd rather do another parachute jump!'

'Well as you like, but I'll be around. We can exchange phone numbers before we finish.'

'I live with my family, but you can contact me at work. They know me as "Sonny" there.'

'But your name is Sanjay. Why do you let them call you Sonny? Don't you see? That diminishes you.'

'I don't mind.' He said it almost in resignation.

I felt despair for him, but hoped that I had given him a push along the road to self-discovery, although I doubted it. He needed to take responsibility for himself, as Martha had said; something we should all do.

There was a lot of emotion and many tears shed during those six days, and at the end, we held an impassioned candlelit graduation ceremony with much hugging and agreement on the positive experience of the seminar. By then, I had swallowed my cynicism and was a convert. Most of all

I had learnt to love myself. It was true after all. Fall in love with yourself and you start a lifelong affair.

It was a week later when I got a surprise phone call from Sanjay, asking if he could visit me.

From his first visit and many subsequent visits, our relationship developed into a love affair, with Sanjay expressing joy and emotion in, what was for him, a new-found experience and fulfilment. Previously hesitant about travelling outside his comfort zone which, geographically, was London and, mentally, his own imposed restrictions, we now took holidays together and toured the country. As Sanjay was happy to admit, it opened his eyes to a country he was not really familiar with, despite having lived all of his adult life in it.

On occasions we were confronted with discrimination at a bed and breakfast guest house. Whether it was because we were two men asking for a double bedroom, or because one of us was coloured, was never clear, but Sanjay always construed it as colour prejudice.

During the next three years we developed a trusting and loving friendship, and Sanjay opened up to his new-found sexuality, but still had not come out to his family. He admitted to me that he still felt a family pressure to conform to their expectations of him and to marry.

'That is something only you can decide,' was my reaction.

I was not prepared to influence him any further. He had experienced an alternative lifestyle with me and he had a choice, but he was still unsure of himself.

Within weeks he told me that his family wanted him to meet a 'suitable' woman they had somehow conjured up for him and not long afterwards I was introduced to a diminutive, friendly, prospective Indian bride named Shahana. Apparently she had been known to the family and approved by them, before being introduced to Sanjay who then agreed to marry her. It was more to fulfil his family's expectations, which he claimed had his best interests at heart, and practically, was it not best to go along with it? She would make a serious, educated, working wife and be a traditional homemaker and comforter for him. What more could he ask for he wanted to know?

'There will be no children,' he said as if to reassure me, but I refrained from questioning the implications of the remark.

I declined the invitation to be his 'best man', but I did accept the invitation to the wedding and, in doing so, accepted his decision to retreat into the comfort of conformity and family approval.

'Our friendship does not have to end because of my marriage,' said Sanjay before the marriage ceremony.

But it did, although there were no recriminations. After accepting Theo's marriage, and now Sanjay's, I felt that I was fighting conformity or denial by homosexual men. I had compromised my own values enough and drew a line at again being the third person in a marriage.

Now I knew that I had to take control of my own life and not to leave it to the decisions of others, or to the whims of fate. I needed to enlarge my own world and circle of friends. I had heard that there was a gay group called 'Phoenix'. How appropriate, I thought, 'That's me; a phoenix rising from the ashes!' I joined, paid my subscription, and found that I was not the only member whose wings had been singed over the years. Its founder, an elderly gay man incorporated it with a gay introduction service. Members also met to dine and socialise at a restaurant in Chelsea. Subscribers to the 'Phoenix' pamphlet, which circulated amongst members, advertised themselves and their preferences for a partner under a box number, and replies were forwarded on to them.

It was in response to an advertisement that I met Ramon, a Spanish artist living in Chelsea with a day job at the Tate. I quickly recognised my other half, despite, or because of, the eighteen years age difference. My penchant for younger men of a different nationality was affirmed. Many gay men look for a mirror image of themselves. I was always more interested in differences of age, culture, and experiences. Ramon had left Spain in 1971, despairing of the oppressive and backward regime of Franco, to live in England and supported himself by kitchen work in restaurants, while he learnt the language. He then took a degree course in art and found his mark as an abstract artist.

We had a mutual attraction for each other which developed into a loving partnership over the following year. By then I knew that I had found my soulmate and we would only be happy living together. Ramon gave up his Chelsea flat and moved in with me and our compatibility has been tested and confirmed ever since. Love is when you know that your life would be incomplete without the other person.

5th December 2005 was a historic day for gay people, when, for the first time in the UK, we had the right to a legally binding relationship which Ramon and I happily embraced in February 2006. I had many loves along the way and most of them were against the law, but now the final one, had come with government approval.

POSTSCRIPT

The world I was born into in 1929 has unquestionably changed for the better. People now have access to a wider world, whether through the TV screen, the computer, mobile phones, car ownership, holidays abroad, or higher education and are consequently better informed. They also have more freedom to question, for self expression and for social mobility.

In my formative years in the 1930s, I knew I was working class, mainly because of what I did not have. I would have been delighted to have gone to a grammar school but that desire was suppressed because it did not fit in with my parents' preconceptions and, consequently, my own. In 1943 I was considered lucky to have missed the proposed new minimum school leaving age of fifteen, enabling me to start work at fourteen and so contribute to the household budget.

Parents are now much more involved in their children's interests, prepared to discuss issues with them and to demonstrate their love. The constraints on pre-nuptial sex have been loosened with sex more openly discussed. I was aware of my predilection for my own sex at puberty but, from then onwards, I felt ashamed to reveal my inclinations, knowing that my parents would have been distressed and would not have understood. My adolescent confusion over my sexual orientation led me to explore the nebulous byways of homoerotic experiences and confirmed my self knowledge that I was homosexual.

My parents, Jim and Beat, lived until 68 and 74 years respectively, still devoted to each other and much loved by their children. When I saw my father for the last time it was in a convalescent home where I was able to take hold of him and hug him. It was an embrace that had been missing all our lives. He said he did not want people visiting his grave and asked to be cremated. His body had to be taken to Blackpool, a place he had always refused to take us as children. My mother lived her last six years a widow and despite having given birth to ten children, died alone. She had a pen and paper by her side, but her heart gave out before she could write what she intended. My brothers and sisters are no more, but live on in my memory and through their inheritance to me, the love of my many nephews and nieces.

Some physical aspects of my childhood still remain. 'The Buildings', where I was born, still stand, stark and affirming their working class origins, but now seemingly devoid of street life and community. The neighbourhood beaches still attract hardened sunbathers when the westerly wind is not blowing, but are relatively deserted as most people fly off to more exotic places. The wide tree-lined streets still proclaim the vision of Barrow's 19th-century planners. The slag heap, with its little train disgorging the hot slag lighting up the night sky with a red glow, has been demolished, the slag recycled and the area landscaped. Retail parks and a leisure complex have replaced the old iron and steel works which daily spewed out their obnoxious gases. A few ghosts from the past still linger in the town but diminish with each visit and will soon be gone forever.

The national demise of Woolworths, when some 30,000 employees lost their jobs, was for me the most unexpected change. From its boom times of the 1950s, when I joined the company, to its growth to over a thousand stores thirty-five years later, when I left, it had given and inspired loyalty, and mapped out my career, but is now just another of my life's tales.